Photoshop in 4 Colors

Second edition

Mattias Nyman

Peachpit Press

Photoshop in 4 Colors

Mattias Nyman

translated by Everett M. Ellestad / INTENSE AB

Originally published in Sweden by Software Plus Scandinavia AB

Copyright © 1991, 1993, 1995 Mattias Nyman / Software Plus Scandinavia AB

Peachpit Press, Inc.

2414 Sixth Street

Berkeley, CA 94710

510/548-4393

510/548-5991

Find us on the World Wide Web at: http://www.peachpit.com

Peachpit Press is a division of Addison-Wesley Publishing Company.

Graphic design and production: Mattias Nyman, Anders Blomberg / ElectroPix

Cover design: TMA Ted Mader Associates

Illustrations: John Dranger, Anders Blomberg / ElectroPix, Anders F. Rönnblom / Studio Matchbox

ISBN: 0-201-88424-0

Printed and bound in Sweden

Contents

Introduction

Rapid technological developments in the field of electronic photo reproduction, including the yearly arrival of new program versions, require this book be updated on a regular basis. In this second, revised U.S. edition I describe some of the new features of Photoshop 3.0.

Whether or not you have read the earlier version of *Photoshop in 4 Colors* (previously entitled *Four Colors/One Image*), you will find the current volume full of useful information about modern image processing.

The focus of this book is on producing high-quality color output in a desktop publishing environment. I describe the basics of color theory and show how to utilize them in Photoshop, QuarkXPress and PageMaker. I also include directions for proceeding step-by-step through everyday processing tasks.

I hope that all who seek knowledge of electronic photo reproduction will find it here.

Mattias Nyman
Stockholm, Sweden
May 1995

Printing

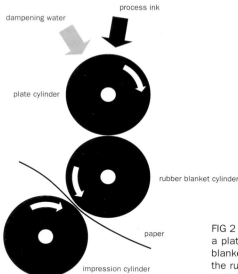

process ink

dampening water

plate cylinder

rubber blanket cylinder

paper

impression cylinder

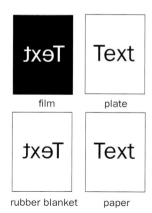

film

plate

rubber blanket

paper

FIG 1 If an offset plate for negative film is used, the image on the film should be negative and reversed with the emulsion-side up. The image on the plate will come out positive and right-reading. The image on the rubber blanket will be positive and reversed. The image on the paper will then be right-reading and positive.

FIG 2 The offset litho process. Process ink and water are applied to a plate attached to a cylinder. The plate presses against a rubber blanket wrapped around another cylinder. The image transferred to the rubber blanket is, in turn, transferred to the paper fed between the rubber blanket cylinder and the impression cylinder.

A number of different printing processes exist for transferring images onto paper. A few of them are letterpress, lithography, gravure and screen (also called silk-screen). The most common process nowadays is a litho process usually known as offset.

In the offset process, the original image is transferred onto a printing plate attached to the plate cylinder of the press. The image areas of the plate are treated to become hydrophobic, and the nonprinting areas are made hydrophilic. Water and ink are then applied to the cylinder. The greasy ink adheres to the hydrophobic surfaces, and the water keeps the non-image surfaces ink-free. In the next step, the image is transferred onto a rubber blanket wrapped around another cylinder. Finally, the image is printed onto the paper that is fed between the blanket cylinder and an impression cylinder.

For multi-color printing—four color, for example—the paper has to pass through as many presses as there are colors. Either each color is allowed to dry before being fed into the next press, or all of the colors are printed onto the paper in rapid succession, a process called wet-on-wet.

The paper is normally run through the presses in two different ways: either sheet-fed or web-fed. Web-fed offset, in which the paper runs off a reel of paper, is the most common method for printing newspapers and catalogs. Sheet-fed offset is most commonly used for high quality printing.

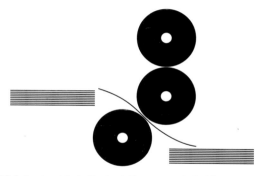

FIG 3 In sheet-fed offset printing, paper is fed from a stack of individual sheets.

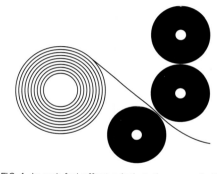

FIG 4 In web-fed offset printing, the paper is fed from a reel.

Screens

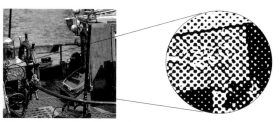

FIG 5 The small halftone dots create an optical illusion of a continuous-tone image.

FIG 6 Four separate screened images in the four process inks: cyan, magenta, yellow and black, or **CMYK** for short. Together they create a complete range of color.

Reproduction is the process of transferring an original photo or illustration onto a printing plate. This is primarily done in two stages: First a halftone image is produced on transparent photographic film. This film is then contact-copied onto the printing plate.

Since offset litho is a binary process—either ink is printed on the paper or it is not—the countless gray shades or color tones of the original must be simulated in some way. This is done by halftone screening. The image is differentiated into a number of dots of varying sizes, each corresponding to the various tones of the original. The many dots create an illusion of a continuous tone image.

Printed color images are built up of four separate screen images, one for each process ink color: cyan, magenta, yellow and black. Theoretically, the first three should be enough, but these colors have certain deficiencies that make it difficult to produce a true black. Black is used to produce good contrast.

Screen frequency (also referred to as screen ruling) is a measure of the proximity of the centers of the dots. The higher the frequency, the finer the screen and the better the reproduced continuous tone image. The frequency cannot be too great, however, since the dots will tend to run together on paper. The result is a reduction in contrast range: the image becomes darker, and details in the darker areas of the image disappear.

Whether a coarse or fine screen should be used depends on the quality of the paper and the printing process. Paper manufacturers can often recommend a suitable screen frequency. The tonal range of the original also affects the choice of screen frequency. A light original that is printed on coated paper in a sheet-fed offset press can be screened with a higher frequency than a dark original that is printed on newspaper in a web-fed press.

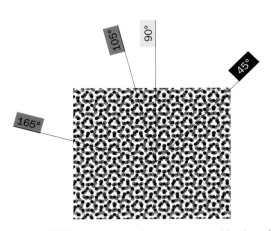

FIG 7 An example of a common combination of screen angles. Since yellow is the weakest color, it is placed only 15 degrees from cyan. All other colors are separated by at least 30 degrees.

FIG 8 If incorrect screen angles are used, an interference, or moiré, pattern will be created. This can be seen as square-like patterns in the photo.

When printing color images, all the colors (except the one printed first) are partially printed on top of one another. In order to ensure that as much ink as possible is printed directly on the paper, the various screens are given different angles. It is important that the correct angle be used. If not, a moiré pattern may result that will adversely affect the quality of the image.

Figure 7 shows some commonly used screen angles. Various screen angle combinations can be used, depending on the dominant image color. The dominant color is printed at the best angle: 45 degrees, which is the angle least visible to the eye. In separation processes currently used, it is usually the black separation that is dominant.

A round halftone dot is most often used, but other shapes are available: elliptical, square and line halftone screens are a few of the more common. The elliptical dot produces smoother color transitions but also larger dot gain during printing. Line screens are used for special effects.

All electronic reproduction work uses digital halftone screens. Digital halftones are built up of small square matrices, and therefore cannot be rotated to any angle in all screen frequencies. The fact that it may not be possible to choose exactly the desired angle and frequency may create moiré patterns. To solve this problem, three principle halftone screen systems have been introduced on the PostScript market: Agfa Balanced Screening Technology (ABS), Adobe Accurate Screening and HQS Screening from Linotype-Hell. These systems all produce excellent results and help avoid moiré patterns.

The halftone screen to be used depends on the output. Linotronic's imagesetter uses HQS, while Agfa's uses ABS and output devices compatible with PostScript Level 2 use Adobe Accurate Screening.

Halftone settings can be stored along with the image file, which is stored in EPS or DCS format. Most often these settings are not necessary; instead, the RIP defines the screen angles and frequency. One reason to store halftone settings would be to have varying screen frequencies and angles appear on the same page.

In Photoshop, the halftone settings can be adjusted using the *Screens* dialog box, which is found under the button of the same name in the *Page Setup* dialog box.

FIG 9 For this photo, a screen frequency of 75 lpi was used.

FIG 10 For this photo, a screen frequency of 120 lpi was used.

RIP

This is an abbreviation for Raster Image Processor—the machine that transforms DTP program instructions, stored in PostScript language, into language the imagesetting equipment can understand.

PostScript

This is a page description language used to describe how a page is built up of various objects (copy, lines, images). It is becoming the *de facto* standard in the graphics industry.

FIG 11 For this photo, a screen frequency of 150 lpi was used.

Recommended screen frequencies for offset printing

Lines per inch (lpi)	Suitable for
75–85	Newspaper, board
100	Wood-free paper, coated wood-containing paper
133–150	Coated paper
150–250	Art paper or double-coated paper

Resolution

FIG 12 The original photo contains a continuous-tone image. It is neither screened nor divided into pixels. (It is screened here in order for it to be printed.)

FIG 13 When an image is scanned by the computer, it is divided up into small square pixels. The number of pixels per unit of length is determined by the scanner's resolution.

FIG 14 When the image is screened, four pixels are analyzed. The average value of these four pixels determines the size of the corresponding halftone dot.

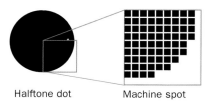

Halftone dot　　　Machine spot

FIG 15 A halftone dot is built up of several small machine spots. The size of these machine spots is determined by the output resolution.

Pixel
An abbreviation of picture element and constitutes the smallest element of a scanned image. Each pixel is a square that is assigned a color or a gray value.

When an original is scanned and stored in a computer, it is transformed into pixels. The scanning resolution is defined as the number of pixels per unit of length, e.g. inches or centimeters.

As long as the number of pixels is constant, the file size remains constant. The resolution can, however, be altered. If it is reduced, the result will be an image that is larger in area, but the file size will remain the same as before. This corresponds to enlarging the image. In other words, the resolution defines only the number of pixels per unit of length.

During output, the image is built up of a number of halftone dots. In order for the transformation from pixels to halftone dots to be the best possible, there must be four times as many pixels as halftone dots, which is to say that the resolution is twice as high as the screen frequency ($2 \cdot 2 = 4$). The resolu-

tion multiplied by the enlargement factor will then provide the necessary scanning resolution.

The doubling of the screen frequency is derived from the "sampling theory." The sampling factor can, however, be reduced from 2 to 1.5, or even lower, if a certain loss of sharpness and detail is acceptable.

If the screen frequency and file size have been set, the latter can be adjusted so that the resolution will not be more than twice the screen frequency. If the resolution is greater, the file size will be greater, and it will take more time to work with and print the image.

The halftone dots of the image are built up of small machine spots produced by the imagesetter. A halftone dot consists of a varying number of machine spots, depending on its size. The number of spots per unit of length is called output resolution.

FIG 16 Here the sampling factor is 0.5—the scanning resolution is 75 dpi, and the screen frequency is 150 lpi.

FIG 17 Here the sampling factor is 1—the scanning resolution is the same as the screen frequency, which in this case is 150 lpi.

FIG 18 Here the sampling factor is 1.5. The scanning frequency is thus 225 dpi, and the screen frequency is 150 lpi.

FIG 19 Here the sampling factor is 2—the ideal ratio between scanning resolution and screen frequency, which are 300 dpi and 150 lpi, respectively.

$$\left(\frac{\text{output resolution}}{\text{screen frequency}}\right)^2 + 1 = \text{number of gray shades (levels)}$$

FIG 20   Use this formula to calculate how many shades of gray can be reproduced for a set output resolution and screen frequency. Below are some examples of how it is used.

$$\left(\frac{2400}{133}\right)^2 + 1 = 325 > 256$$

EXAMPLE 1   An output resolution of 2400 dpi and a screen frequency of 133 lpi will give 325 possible gray shades. This is sufficient for reproducing the 256 shades of gray found in the scanned image.

$$\left(\frac{1200}{75}\right)^2 + 1 = 257 > 256$$

EXAMPLE 2   An output resolution of 1200 dpi and a screen frequency of 75 lpi will give 257 possible gray shades—almost exactly as many as are found in the scanned image.

$$\left(\frac{1270}{85}\right)^2 + 1 = 224 \ \text{(acceptable)}$$

EXAMPLE 3   A common combination is an output resolution of 1270 dpi and a screen frequency of 85 lpi. The result, 224 gray shades, is acceptable since it is close to the 256 gray shades in the image.

FIG 21   Use this formula to determine how high the scanning resolution must be when the size of the original and the size of the printed image are known.

$$\frac{\text{desired size}}{\text{original size}} \times 2 \times \text{screen frequency} = \text{scanning resolution}$$

EXAMPLE 4   To print an image 120 mm wide from a small slide (24 x 36 mm) using a screen frequency of 133 lpi, calculate:

$$\frac{120}{36} \times 2 \times 133 = 887 \text{ dpi}$$

Set to scan with a resolution of at least 887 dpi.

EXAMPLE 5   To print an image 30 cm high from a photo measuring 18 x 24 cm with a screen frequency of 150 lpi, calculate:

$$\frac{30}{24} \times 2 \times 150 = 375 \text{ dpi}$$

Set to scan with a resolution of at least 375 dpi.

FIG 22   To determine how large an image can be printed, use this formula when the number of pixels along one side is known. (If you multiple by 25.4, the result will be in millimeters.)

$$\frac{\text{number of pixels}}{2 \times \text{screen frequency}} = \text{image size in inches}$$

The red digit 2 is derived from the sampling theory. If a certain loss of quality is acceptable, this factor can be reduced to 1.5. In most cases, there will be no noticeable difference (see page 7).

EXAMPLE 6   The photo is 1024 pixels high, and the screen frequency is 85 lpi. To find out how high an image can be printed, calculate:

$$\frac{1024}{2 \times 85} \times 25.4 = 153 \text{ mm}$$

The image can be 153 mm high using a sampling factor of 2. If the sampling factor is reduced, the image can be larger.

The output resolution often cannot be altered much. There are two common fixed resolutions: one close to 1200 dpi and another around 2400 dpi. Choosing one depends on the screen frequency used. To reproduce a four-color image, there needs to be four separate halftones. Each halftone image, one for each process ink, contains a maximum of 256 shades of gray. For these to be reproduced with a set screen frequency, the imagesetter must have a certain resolution.

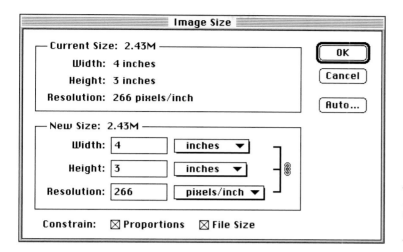

Image Size

─ Current Size: 2.43M ─
  Width: 4 inches
  Height: 3 inches
  Resolution: 266 pixels/inch

[OK]
[Cancel]
[Auto...]

─ New Size: 2.43M ─
  Width: 4   inches ▼
  Height: 3   inches ▼
  Resolution: 266   pixels/inch ▼

Constrain: ☒ Proportions   ☒ File Size

FIG 23 The *Image Size* dialog box from Photoshop. The image has been scanned using a resolution of 266 dpi because the intended screen frequency is 133 lpi. The original is 3 in. high by 4 in. wide.

Image Size

─ Current Size: 2.43M ─
  Width: 4 inches
  Height: 3 inches
  Resolution: 266 pixels/inch

[OK]
[Cancel]
[Auto...]

─ New Size: 2.43M ─
  Width: 3.547   inches ▼
  Height: 2.66   inches ▼
  Resolution: 300   pixels/inch ▼

Constrain: ☒ Proportions   ☒ File Size

FIG 24 The resolution is altered to 300 dpi in order to match a screen frequency of 150 lpi. The image can be made 2.66 in. high by 3.547 in. wide if the sampling factor is to be 2. The number of pixels is the same as in the previous figure.

Image Size

─ Current Size: 2.43M ─
  Width: 4 inches
  Height: 3 inches
  Resolution: 266 pixels/inch

[OK]
[Cancel]
[Auto...]

─ New Size: 3.09M ─
  Width: 4   inches ▼
  Height: 3   inches ▼
  Resolution: 300   pixels/inch ▼

Constrain: ☒ Proportions   ☐ File Size

FIG 25 Here the number of pixels are altered so the resolution and size of the image will be the same. The result is that the file size increases. The new pixels forming the image are created artificially by analyzing the adjacent pixels. The quality of this image will not be as good as if it had been scanned with a resolution of 300 dpi from the start. In that case, no new pixels would have had to have been artificially created.

Color Systems

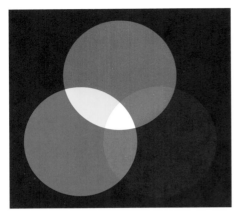

FIG 26 In the additive color system, red, green and blue are the primary colors, and cyan, magenta and yellow are the secondary colors. Red, green and blue together produce white.

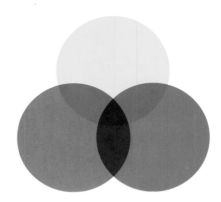

FIG 27 In the subtractive color system, cyan, magenta and yellow are the primary colors, and red, green and blue are the secondary colors. Cyan, magenta and yellow produce black.

Tertiary Colors
These are colors built up of components of all three process colors. Most of the colors in an image are tertiary colors.

For color reproduction in a DTP environment, three different systems are used to describe color. The additive and subtractive systems describe a color's relative composition of three primary colors. The third system, the CIE system, is an absolute system in which a particular color is assigned three numerical coordinates in a color model.

The additive color system uses combinations of red, green and blue to produce all the colors of the spectrum. (Equal parts of red, green and blue light create white light.) This is the system that is used for scanning an image and reproducing it on a monitor. The intensity of minute red, green and blue dots on the monitor is varied electronically to build up an image. The additive color system also represents a good method for measuring how the eye sees colors. It is usually called the RGB model, taken from the first letters of each primary color.

The subtractive color system uses cyan, magenta and yellow. Mixing these colors in near-equal parts creates black. This system is the foundation of the art of printing. Cyan, magenta and yellow are called process colors. In Europe, they are defined as the Euroscale. In the U.S.A., they are defined according to SWOP standards. These two definitions are somewhat different, especially regarding cyan.

The most serious fault of the subtractive system is that 100% of cyan, magenta and yellow do not produce a true, solid black but rather a dark brown. For this reason, black is added in practice, and the system is thus called CMYK (K stands for Key Color).

In both the additive and the subtractive color systems, the numerical definitions of the colors depend on the properties and appearances of the primary colors used. For example, a particular color that is composed of 20% red, 30% green and 50% blue will appear somewhat different depending on how the red, green and blue primaries actually look. Such a difference can be found, for instance, between two different monitor screens.

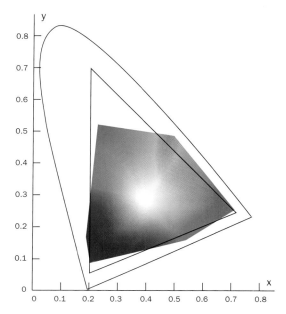

FIG 28 The chromaticity diagram of the CIEXYZ system. The color area represents the colors that can be printed on coated paper. The black triangle encompasses the colors that can be reproduced on a monitor. The outer curved line encompasses colors the eye can see. (Colors in the illustration are approximate.)

FIG 29 The European process inks have been assigned the following coordinates in the CIE system.

	C	M	Y
x	0.153	0.464	0.437
y	0.196	0.232	0.494
Y	21.9	17.1	77.8

The actual color coordinates of the inks also depend on what they are to be used for. Inks for newsprint differ substantially from those intended for better paper qualities. Even the process inks from different manufacturers vary. How RGB data are converted to CMYK data is determined by the parameters for process inks entered into the separation program used.

Other color standards exist—for instance, the American SWOP, in which colors have been assigned other coordinates.

It is advantageous to have a color system with primaries that are standardized and fixed. Such a standardized descriptive color system is the CIEXYZ system. This is a system in which the three basic colors (red, green and blue) have been systematically chosen and assigned special coordinates. They therefore constitute fixed points in the system.

In a CIE system, all pure hues are plotted along a curve in the x-y plane. Perpendicular to this surface is a Y-axis representing lightness of color, with greater lightness toward the top.

A variation of the CIEXYZ system is called CIELAB. It is designed to be perceptually uniform—that is, equal movements within the color space are perceived by the eye as equal differences in color. This is not the case with the original CIEXYZ system.

In both the RGB system and the CMYK system, there are limitations as to what colors can be repro-duced. Unfortunately, the reproducible colors vary for the two systems. This causes difficulties when a color image is to be converted from one system to the other. Some colors simply cannot be reproduced in both systems and must therefore be approximated by some adjacent color.

If a CIE system is used as a basis for all conversion calculations, it is possible to take the various properties of (for example) the scanner, monitor, color printer and process inks into consideration. Examples of such properties are the type of phosphor used in the monitor, the hue error (or contaminant color) of the process inks and the density of the printer's colors.

In order for the colors displayed on the screen to match the printed colors as closely as possible, it is important that all the components of the system be calibrated and finely tuned.

FIG 30 Color tinges show up as faint, undesirable hues throughout the entire photo. Color tinges can occur if the lighting conditions are wrong for the type of film used. Most slide films tend to produce faint color tinges that vary from film to film.

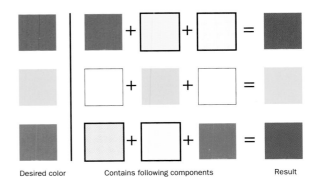

Desired color   Contains following components   Result

FIG 31 Separation filters and process inks are far from perfect. The various shortcomings add up to colors that are impure. The above illustration is exaggerated. The framed areas represent the undesirable elements that result in hue error, or contaminated colors.

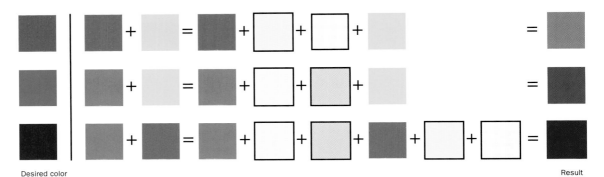

Desired color   Result

FIG 32 This is how the secondary colors are affected by deficiencies in separation filters and process inks. To the left are the desired colors. To the right are the resultant colors, and in between is shown how the colors are built up. The framed areas represent the undesirable color elements. Note that the illustration is highly exaggerated.

The deficiencies of the colors in the CMYK system have created a need for a general color correction of images. Impurities in the process inks and deficiencies in separation filter transmission and absorption bring about contaminant colors that must be compensated for. Yellow is, for the most part, correct. Cyan, on the other hand, contains a considerable amount of magenta and a smaller amount of yellow. Magenta has some yellow and a small trace of cyan.

Furthermore, color correction may be necessary to remove color tinges found in the original, or simply to change the appearance of the image compared with the original. Frequently, there is a desire to make an illustration more attractive than the original—such as making the grass greener or the sky bluer.

The most important colors in an image are the so-called memory colors, colors that we easily recognize and object to if they are wrong. Typical examples are skin colors, grass greens and orange oranges. It is necessary to do color corrections that make these colors look right.

For optimal reproduction of most colors, a high-gloss paper with a high whiteness and smoothness is best. The legibility of black letters is, however, highest on a paper with a slightly uneven surface structure and a somewhat yellow hue. This means the choice of paper for printed matter containing both words and images is always a compromise. In addition, other factors, such as availability, finances and graphic design, affect the choice of paper. The adaptability of the reproduction process makes the choice of paper easier.

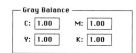

Gray Balance

C: 1.00   M: 1.00

Y: 1.00   K: 1.00

FIG 34 In Photoshop, the gray balance is often altered using these data. The value is initially 1.00 and this produces a good gray balance in most cases. If a value is reduced, the amount of that color decreases (its curve in figure 35 drops).

FIG 33 Three gray scales. The one to the left is built up of only the primary colors and has a correct gray balance. The middle one is composed of only black and can be used as a reference. The right one has too much magenta. It will produce a color tinge.

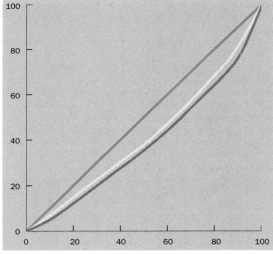

FIG 35 This is how a correct gray balance should look. Cyan is often used as a guideline for the desired gray value.

FIG 36 The lower half of the photo has a correct gray balance, and the upper half has an incorrect gray balance.

Neutral shades of gray are produced by mixing the three primary colors, cyan, magenta and yellow, in approximately equal proportions. Because of contaminant colors in the process inks, a certain amount of correction must be done to produce gray shades that are truly neutral. The gray balance is the amount of the three colors that must be used to create a neutral gray.

A correct gray balance is necessary to produce good separations. If the gray balance is not correct, the entire image is affected—even those parts that are not gray. Shifts in hue occur in the image, and many of the colors look strange.

A balanced gray scale is created and printed in order to check the gray balance. As a comparison, a gray scale of black incorporating the same shade levels can be used.

In Photoshop, the gray balance can be adjusted under the *Printing Inks Setup* dialog box by choosing the *Custom* setting for process ink definitions. A change in the gray balance can be seen if the neutral gray shades are read with the eyedropper as well as on the curve in the *Separation Setup* dialog box. The gray balance, however, normally does not need to be adjusted.

Tonal Range

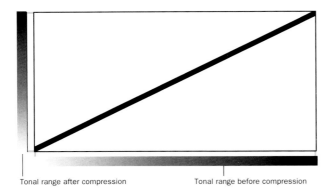

Tonal range after compression   Tonal range before compression

FIG 37 Tone compression takes place by compressing the original tonal range (the horizontal axis) down to the resultant tonal range (the vertical axis). When compression takes place along a straight line, it is called linear.

Color slide	2.7
Coated paper (high quality)	2.2
Paper print (b&w)	1.8
Paper print (color)	1.8
Coated paper (normal quality)	1.6
Newsprint	0.9

FIG 38 Above are some approximate tonal ranges for common originals and paper qualities.

Image type	Highlight	Shadow
Light	3%	98%
Midtone	2%	97%
Dark	1%	96%

FIG 39 This table shows the tonal limits for various image types. The data apply to the image on the film and printing on coated paper.

A color original often has a large tonal range: the difference between the lightest and the darkest tones. This is about 2.7 for a color slide and about 2.0 for a paper print, as expressed in a logarithmic density scale. Such a wide tonal range is impossible to reproduce in printing since colors cannot be printed on paper with the same high density as film tones. On very high quality paper, used rarely, it is possible to reproduce a tonal range of about 1.9. Most printed matter has paper qualities that can withstand a tonal range of about 1.5. Newspaper has a range as low as 0.9, so during reproduction work, the tonal range must be compressed, the tones shaded closer to one another. Closely similar tones are merged into a single tone. For this reason, it is important to study the original, determine which areas are the most important, and note their tonal range. Then the reproduction process can be optimized for these areas.

The tonal range of the printed image varies according to the quality of the paper and the density of the inks. Normally efforts are made to restrict the tonal ranges of the printed image in both the highlights and shadows. This is done so that the printed image does not look eroded in the diffuse highlight areas and excessively thick in the darkest areas. The limits in figure 39 serve as a good recommendation. An exception must be made for small white surfaces that really are white—called specular highlights—and small surfaces that are to be totally black. The recommended limits apply to tonal values in the printed image. In the film, the tonal values must be somewhat less in order to compensate for changes in tone (see page 46).

Another method for restricting tonal range is to set the limits so that all of the tonal values below a certain level (about 5%) are made white and all the tonal values over a certain level (about 95%) are made black. This increases the image's contrast and may work well in printing on newspaper. The best method must be found by trial and error, and a combination of the two can be used.

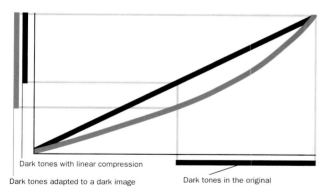

Dark tones with linear compression

Dark tones adapted to a dark image

Dark tones in the original

FIG 40 Here tone compression has been adapted for a dark image. The dark tones in the original have been given a range greater than half the available tones. The gamma number for such a curve is higher than 1.0.

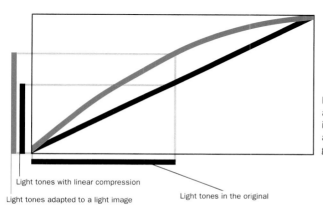

Light tones with linear compression

Light tones adapted to a light image

Light tones in the original

FIG 41 If tone compression does not take place along a straight line, it is nonlinear. If compression is to be adjusted for light images, the light tones are given greater tonal range than the dark. The gamma number for such a curve is less than 1.0.

Compression of the original photo's tonal range is done during scanning. At that time the tonal curve can be adjusted to match the image type in question—normally using a gamma value. Gamma values determine the way in which tonal compression takes place. A higher gamma value means a less linear compression, which results in more tonal steps being given to the darker tonal regions.

The best gamma value for simulating how our eyes see tones is about 1.8. For this reason, 1.8 is a suitable gamma value both for scanning a normal midtone image and for adjusting your monitor. A light photo should, in other words, be scanned using a gamma value lower than 1.8, and a dark photo using a gamma value higher than 1.8. It is also possible to use curve shapes other than the gamma curve when scanning a photo. Other desirable results can then be achieved, such as high contrast or a better reproduction of details in a specific tonal range.

It is important that the program you use can correctly interpret the values sent by the scanner.

This means that the program must be set using the same gamma value that is used for scanning normal photos. Getting the scanned image to look like the original requires that your monitor also be set for the correct gamma value.

Adapting the repro process to actual circumstances is necessary to obtain good results. Some of the factors that affect how an image is processed are: what elements are important in the photo, what the photo should convey, what paper grade is to be used for printing, and how extensive the tonal value changes that occur during output and printing will be. To achieve the best results, it is necessary to have knowledge of all the steps in the production chain.

For the results to be predictable and repeatable, the process has to be standardized and the integral components calibrated. The goal is for the same settings to produce the same results time after time. Such a stable system is necessary for achieving high quality.

Scanners

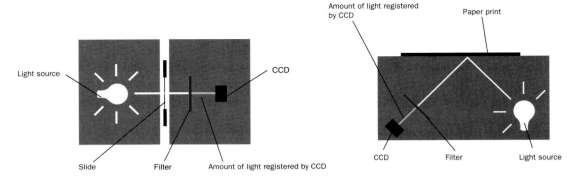

FIG 42 The basic principle of a slide scanner. The light passes through the slide and then a filter. After that, the remaining light is registered by CCD photodiodes.

FIG 43 The basic principle of a scanner for paper prints. Light is reflected from the print and passes through a filter. Then the remaining light is registered by the CCD photodiodes.

An original is converted into pixels using a scanner. There are scanners for various kinds of original artwork—slides or paper prints. Some scanners work with both slides and prints.

Light is transmitted through a slide or reflected off a paper print. This transmitted or reflected light passes through color filters that separate the red, green and blue wavelengths. The light then reaches CCD cells that sense the intensity of the light and feed the data to the computer. CCD stands for Charge-Coupled Device, an array of photodiodes for converting light into digital data.

If the CCD cells work with 8 bits, the device sends out numerical values between 0 and 255 ($2^8 = 256$). This is done three times, once for each color filter. There are now CCD arrays on the market that sense the intensity of the three colors simultaneously; they do not require three filtered scans.

The number of CCD photodiodes per unit of length determines the scanner resolution. If there are 300 photodiodes per inch, the scanner has a resolution of 300 dpi (dots per inch).

The optical precision of the scanner determines how good the sharpness and color reproduction are. High optical precision means that a pixel-size area of the original is registered on exactly one CCD photodiode. The result is excellent sharpness and pure colors. Low precision means that adjacent photodiodes will partially register the same data, with poor sharpness and impure colors as the result.

The mechanical precision (registration) of a scanner must be good if each scan is to be exactly the same for each color. Poor mechanical precision may result in extra lines and color aberrations being added to the image.

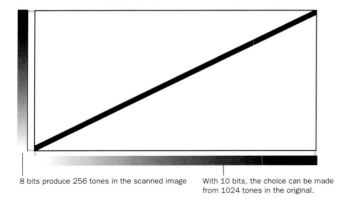

8 bits produce 256 tones in the scanned image

With 10 bits, the choice can be made from 1024 tones in the original.

FIG 44 If a scanner is able to read off more tones than can be stored in the computer, you can make a selection of tones that is optimized for the tone distribution of the original.

FIG 45 This image contains many tones. The range is good in both the light and dark areas.

FIG 46 This image contains few tones. The range is poor in both the light and dark areas.

A computer works with 8 bits per pixel per color. This means that each pixel is allocated one of the $2^8 = 256$ tones in each color: red, green and blue. This is called a 24-bit color depth, since $2^8 \cdot 2^8 \cdot 2^8 = 2^{24} = 16,777,216$ different color tones for each pixel.

If the CCD's photodiodes have a greater color depth than 8 bits, they will be able to differentiate more tones, which creates a greater dynamic range. Some scanners work with a 10-bit depth, or even more, which allows $2^{10}=1024$ tones per color and pixel. The advantage here is that the choice of 256 tones can be adapted according to the tone distribu-tion of the original. A second advantage of scanning an original using more tones than necessary is that interference during scanning can be filtered out.

There are numerous manufacturers of scanners for DTP environments. An alternative to investing in a scanner is to use the Kodak Photo CD System. This system allows a conventional photo lab to handle the scanning and then to supply the image stored on a Photo CD as well as on negatives and slides. To access the image on the disc, you will need a CD-ROM drive connected to your computer, as well as the necessary software.

Original Classification

FIG 47 This is a typical snow image. There are many diffuse details in the limestone walls of the light areas. In the dark areas of the image, the balconies and windows, there are no important details.

FIG 48 A typical night image is shown above. The rider's clothes and details of the motorcycle are distinguishable in the dark areas. Details of the engine and helmet may be overexposed. The idea is to adjust the scanning parameters to bring out the dark areas as much as possible without causing the engine and helmet details to disappear.

It is very important for subsequent image manipulation that the scanned image be as high-quality as possible. It is easy to correct a well-scanned image to make it even better, but it is almost impossible to enhance one that was poorly scanned.

As mentioned above, tone compression takes place during scanning. For this reason, the scanning parameters should be set so that the details in the more important areas of the original are picked up. This may mean that other, less important, details disappear. For example, giving priority to the shadow tones may cause the highlight tones to disappear.

The gamma value controls which tonal areas in the image will be reproduced best. A dark original should be scanned with a higher gamma value than a light one. A high gamma value allows more of the available tones to reproduce dark areas (see page 15).

To facilitate handling, it is useful to classify the original's tone distribution before scanning. Originals can be divided into three classes: snow images, midtone images and night images. (Sometimes the terms "high-key," "medium" and "low-key" are used.) This applies to both color and black and white.

Snow-image originals are characterized by about 70% to 90% of the image being taken up by light areas in which the most important details are found. Light tones are also called diffuse highlight tones. The wholly white areas in the image are called specular highlights.

In midtone originals, the light and dark areas each take up about half of the image area, and the details are found in the midtone areas—tones between about 30% and 70% of white. Normally there is an absence of details in the light and dark areas.

Night images consist mainly of dark tones, and the details are found in these dark areas. Dark tones are also known as shadow tones (or shadows).

FIG 49 Above is a midtone photo with numerous details and rather high contrast. The differences between light and dark tones are considerable. To the right is a midtone photo with low contrast and only a few fine details.

Classification, in other words, is not simply determining details in the lighter areas but determining which areas of the original convey the main message.

Midtone originals are the easiest to reproduce. Snow images are also quite easy. The most important consideration with these originals is not to scan them so light that the details in the light areas disappear.

Night images are the most difficult. This is because most scanners on the market work with CCD technology. These devices have difficulty differentiating between similar tones in the dark areas. This type of original is also the hardest to reproduce on a printing press.

A good deal of time and effort should be directed toward learning to choose the right types of originals, learning how to classify them, and to finding the correct scanning settings. These settings can typically be saved under distinctive names. When an original is to be scanned at a later time, you need only classify the image and then retrieve the proper file to set the scanner. This leads to greater simplification and efficiency.

Some types of originals may be difficult to scan with standard settings, but it is easiest to start with settings that are close and modify them a little—for example, to compensate for color tinges.

It is always best to make adjustments as early in the production process as possible. This is why great care should be taken to get the best possible scan. That way, fewer corrections need to be made in the image-manipulation program.

File Formats

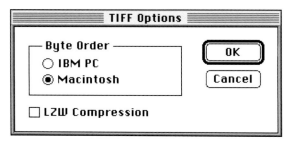

FIG 50 The TIFF format was designed to help transport images between IBM PC and Macintosh computers. An image can also be compressed using LZW compression. This nondestructive method causes the image to take up a little less space on the hard disk. For this compression method to be useful, the program in which the image will be used must be able to load compressed images. QuarkXPress can read LZW-compressed images, but it takes more time to load them than if they were not compressed.

Images that are scanned into a computer can be stored in a number of formats. A format is a specific way to describe an image for computers so that it can be saved on a hard disk. An overview of the five most important formats, and what can be expected from them, is presented below.

Photoshop format is Photoshop's default format for saving files if no other format is stipulated. One advantage to using this format is that the images are compressed automatically and thus take up relatively little space on a hard disk. A disadvantage is that images in Photoshop format cannot be imported into page-layout programs. Images in both RGB and CMYK modes can be saved in Photoshop format.

TIFF-RGB format can be used to transfer images into other programs. Images in this format cannot

be separated in CMYK mode. If they are to be printed out as separated colors, the importing program must have this capability. The advantages of the TIFF-RGB format are that it is relatively standardized, takes up little disk space, and is easy to compress, causing the images to take up even less disk space.

TIFF-CMYK format is nearly the same as TIFF-RGB, with the difference that the images are separated in CMYK mode. All the separation settings and compensation data for tonal value changes have therefore already been taken care of. These images require one third more memory than TIFF-RGB format images. Transfer functions cannot be saved with images in any TIFF format.

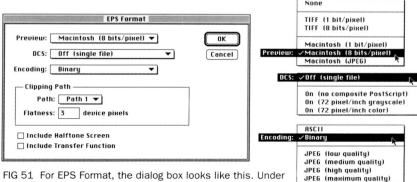

FIG 51 For EPS Format, the dialog box looks like this. Under *Preview*, it is possible to choose whether the preview image is to be in TIFF (for PC) or PICT (for Macintosh) and whether it is to be displayed in black and white (1 bit/pixel) or color (8 bits/pixel). You can also choose whether the preview image should be JPEG compressed. Under *Encoding*, you can choose whether the PostScript data should be ASCII or binary coded. Binary is the most common form and is often recommended. Here it is also possible to choose JPEG compression. It is then saved in EPS-JPEG format. Under *"Desktop Color Separation"* (DCS), you can create a five-file EPS format and choose whether color information for proofing on a color printer is included. In the box entitled *Clipping Path*, you can stipulate which path in the document is to be used as the clipping path to create, for example, a transparent background when background stripping. If the path has been entered in the *Paths* palette, it will already be displayed here. At the bottom of the dialog box, you can choose whether data concerning halftone screens and transfer functions are to be saved in the file.

EPS format images consist of PostScript data that define the image and a preview image (PICT for Macintosh and TIFF for IBM PC format) of low resolution that is shown on the monitor screen. So that the file does not take up unnecessary memory or disk space, only the low-resolution image is saved as part of the file when the image is mounted on a page. The preview image is linked to PostScript data that is addressed during output. Although the mounted image is of low resolution, color reproduction is relatively good. If the image is saved in TIFF-CMYK format, the importing program must convert the color information back into RGB data, which can cause rather large color deviations if the importing program does not have a color-processing system to handle this.

DCS format is a type of *EPS* format in which the image is divided into five files—one for each color plus a preview image in low resolution linked to the color file. The advantage of this is that the preview image takes up little memory and can easily be distributed over a network. During printout, the color file is automatically addressed. PostScript data can also be saved in the preview image. This can then be used to produce color proofs on a PostScript color printer.

An advantage of both EPS and DCS formats is that the halftone screen settings (see page 5) and the transfer functions can be saved with the image. Transfer functions are tonal curves that alter the tonal value of the image (see page 46).

Proofs

FIG 52 The left photo has a bleed off the right margin, while the right photo has no bleed. A **bleed** occurs when part of the print on a page (often the image) extends beyond the margin and to the edge of the paper.

Things to think about when using color printer proofs

1. Does the printer use PostScript?
2. What paper sizes does the printer use?
3. Can the printer reproduce bleeds?
4. Is the printer's memory sufficient?
5. Does the printer have enough color range to simulate offset printed images?
6. Is the printer fast enough?
7. What different kinds of paper can it use?

The purpose of a proof is to determine how the image will look in print. Proofs can be produced in several ways: by outputting to a color printer; by photographic/electrostatic methods, using separated films; and by printing on a press on regular paper. Printing on regular paper is expensive, but it is clearly the best method since it is done under the same conditions as will be used during production. And it can be economical when producing long runs of expensive printed matter.

Proofs are also used as an important element in placing a printing job. The printing house should be able to duplicate the proof quality, and the customer should be able to use it as a legally binding sample in case of any future claims or complaints regarding printing quality.

Proofs that are not produced in a printing press are called prepress proofs. These are among the most common methods, and use lamination techniques. The four colors—cyan, magenta, yellow and black—are each applied to a base that can simulate the final paper. Then the four bases are laminated together. This creates a laminated proof very close in quality to the final printed image, but the process is somewhat complicated and relatively expensive.

The fastest and least expensive method is to output the image using a color printer. Color printers still have rather low resolution, which means that conventional halftone screening cannot be employed. It is also difficult to achieve a good match between a color printout and the final printed image. However, this problem can be solved by using a system like Apple ColorSync or EfiColor (see page 24).

In the case of laminated prepress proofs, a number of settings, such as those for color reproduction, the various base types, tonal value changes and the different plastic coatings, need to be carefully considered. The colors must agree with the color standard used (Eurostandard or SWOP), and they should have the same density as the final printing.

There are a variety of bases available to simulate the different kinds of paper and the resultant dot gains. The best solution is to use the same kind of paper as will be used in the final printing. It may be possibile to add a final coating to simulate glossy paper or the yellow tone found in newspaper.

When using color printers, you should check the paper size and color range as well as the speed, output stability and amount of memory available.

The paper size should be big enough to allow for bleeds. The color range should be broad enough to adequately simulate the colors of the standard you are using. Color files are often very large, so the output device must have sufficient memory and speed to manage the job.

In judging the proofs, it is important to know how they were produced and what shortcomings the selected method might have. Usually, laminated proofs have a glossy surface that produces highly saturated, distinct colors. When the image is later printed on newsprint, the output is not as good, and the customer is often disappointed. If the right method for pulling the proof is used, and if the customer is made aware of the technical considerations, misunderstandings can be avoided.

Calibration

original   display   print

original   display   print

FIG 53 In a calibrated system, the various units produce the same results from the same original. If the system is absolutely calibrated, the units will produce results exactly the same as the original. This cannot, however, always be demanded, owing to the varying tone and color ranges of the units.

FIG 54 In an uncalibrated system, the various units produce different results from the same original.

Calibration is a process of adjusting the production equipment so that the settings can be recorded and held constant during an extended period.

The devices that need to be calibrated are the scanner, the monitor, the imagesetter and the prepress printer. Of course, one must also calibrate the printing press, the equipment used to produce proofs, and even the printing plates, but this book covers only the links in the production cycle up to the output of film.

Many scanners calibrate themselves when they are turned on, or they come with special calibration software. Calibration includes adjustment of the feeding mechanism for the original or the CCD photodiodes so that the color registration and sharpness are correct. The color balance is also adjusted so that no color tinges are created during scanning.

The monitor is adjusted for satisfactory reproduction of tone and for proper color balance. Tonal values are adjusted with the gamma value. A gamma number of 1.0 represents a linear reproduction of tone. The eye, however, perceives tones on a logarithmic scale, and the dark tones thus seem more compressed than the light ones. This can be simulated on the monitor by raising the gamma value.

Separation programs are calibrated so that the separation (the conversion from RGB to CMYK values) is carried out correctly, taking into consideration the adjustment of the monitor and the output device to be used, as well as other factors.

A supplement to Apple's system software called ColorSync has been developed to help keep track of the devices connected to the system and to administer color conversions between them. Thus, color reproduction is kept the same no matter what output device is used—a monitor, color printer or printing press. ColorSync works by maintaining profiles (special files of properties) for all the system devices.

These profiles describe the color properties of each unit when calibrated. With their help, ColorSync determines how the conversion should be carried out. If Apple's model for color conversion is unsatisfactory, ColorSync can be supplemented with models from independent manufacturers. There are a number of such models on the market. One is EfiColor, developed by Electronics for Imaging, Inc. EfiColor is used by Cachet and some other programs. Another model for color conversion is ColorSense from Kodak.

In Photoshop, the printing inks' CIE definitions can be altered, which affects how the RGB values are converted into CMYK values.

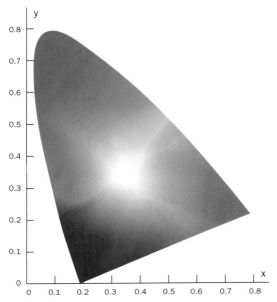

FIG 55 This is a chromaticity diagram of a CIE system encompassing all colors seen by the eye. This diagram actually cannot be printed, since the printable colors are considerably fewer in number (see page 11).

An example of a color-conversion model is EfiColor. An EfiColor Processor file is dropped into the System folder together with a database containing profiles for all of the system's units. Images are stored in the computer with a color description that is dependent on the system used; it does not depend on the various color characteristics of the units. It is called EFI Calibrated RGB and is built on a CIELAB model. When the colors are to be displayed on a monitor, or separated for printing, the colors are converted according to the profile that applies to the unit in question.

Euroscale Very Low	12%
Euroscale Low	17%
Euroscale Medium	23%
Euroscale Medium High	30%

When separating images using EfiColor, find out what dot gain the printing company has and choose the closest profile with the correct ink sets. For offset printing in the U.S. SWOP profiles are suitable.

Ink Colors

	Y	x	y
C:	23.80	0.1636	0.2144
M:	17.11	0.4464	0.2455
Y:	73.33	0.4352	0.4959
MY:	15.98	0.5760	0.37
CY:	16.43	0.2352	0.5536
CM:	4.28	0.2125	0.1481
CMY:	3.16	0.3407	0.3687
W:	86.24	0.3090	0.3244
K:	1.74	0.2991	0.3193

OK Cancel

FIG 56 Assume that you want to compensate for an undesirable element of yellow in magenta, resulting in an orangish red. The values for red (MY) are x=0.5760 and y=0.3349. The red in the photo appears orange-red, so that must be expressed in CIE values. This corresponds to the red hues being closer to the yellow area in the chromaticity diagram. Choose *Custom* and enter y=0.37 instead. You will then see that the red color field becomes more orange. Contaminated colors in the other colors can be compensated for in a similar way.

An alternative method is to measure the printing inks and the combinations of them with an instrument called spectrophotometer. The x-, y- and Y-values can then be entered and saved as a custom printing ink definition. To get a good result with this method, correct solid densities and a well controlled print process is required.

FIG 57 This photo has no extra compensation for contaminated colors.

FIG 58 This photo has been given extra compensation for contaminated colors according to the method described above.

Scanning

In scanning, a number of parameters should be considered: whether scanning is to be in black and white or color; the resolution that will be used; the area to be scanned; and the tone distribution of the original image.

The scanner is controlled either by an independent software package or through a plug-in module to another program. With a plug-in module, you can access the image directly from inside an image-manipulation or page-layout program. In most of the control programs for scanners, a low-resolution image is first scanned and displayed on the monitor. You can then indicate what part of the original is of interest and scan only that part of the image. Images take up a great deal of space on hard disks, which is why it is unwise to store parts of an image that will not be needed.

Next, the scanning resolution should be adjusted for the size and screen frequency of the printed image. Excessive resolution only takes up unnecessary disk space without any improvement in quality. How to calculate the required resolution is explained on page 8 in the section on resolution.

The most difficult step in the scanning procedure is adapting the settings to the tone distribution of the original. After having classified the original (see the section on original classification on page 18), you need to choose a suitable tone curve.

A night image should be scanned with a high gamma value, and a snow image with a low one. A midtone image should have a gamma value near 1.0.

The goal of scanning, and of the subsequent processing, is to produce an image on the monitor that is as close to the desired printed result as possible. Then settings need to be chosen to make this possible. In other words, it is wrong to scan in an image on the light side in order to compensate for later dot gain. Instead, the original should be scanned so that the image on the monitor looks like it will when printed on paper. Then you should correct for dot gain by other means.

FIG 59 This column of images is the way the photos should look when the correct scanning parameters are used.

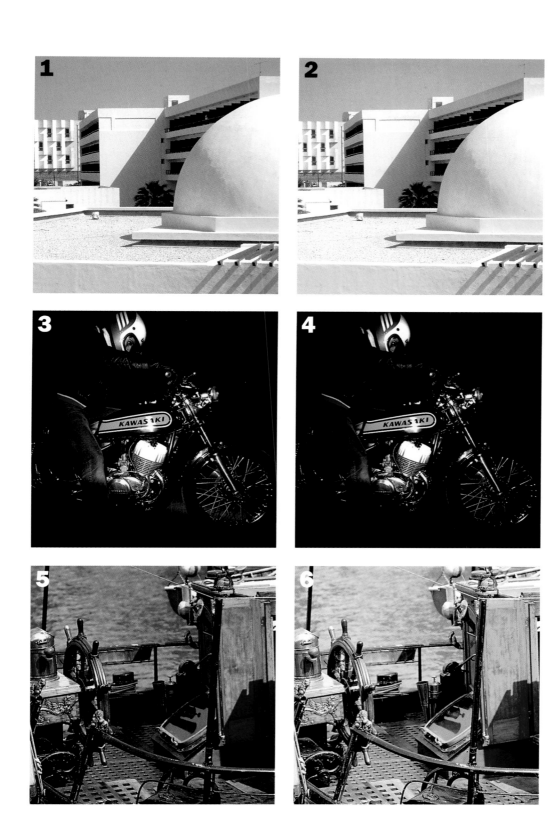

FIG 60 Here you can see how important it is to use the right parameters during scanning. Photos 1 and 3 were scanned as midtone images; photos 2 and 6 as night images; and photos 4 and 5 as snow images. Subsequent attempts to correct for these errors will inevitably produce poorer results than if the correct settings had been used from the start.

Tone Correction

FIG 61 A histogram showing the tone distribution of an image. The dark tones are to the left and the light tones to the right. The height of each bar indicates how many pixels have a certain tonal value (how great an area of the image has a certain tonal value).

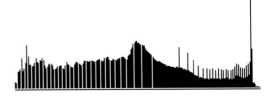

FIG 62 Since the image has been made lighter, the tones have been displaced toward the lighter areas. The white strips and black spikes occur because there are only 256 halftones and these have been redistributed (compressed) into a smaller area.

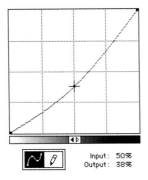

Input: 50%
Output: 38%

FIG 63 A tonal value diagram is used to show how the tonal values of the image have been altered. The original tonal values are on the x-axis; the new tonal values are on the y-axis. In this case, all the pixels having tonal values of 50% are altered to 38%. The other tones in the image change according to the curve.

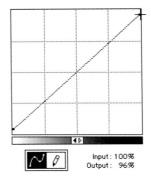

Input: 100%
Output: 96%

FIG 64 This is the way a tonal value diagram looks when the limits of 4% and 96%, respectively, have been introduced for halftone values. The result is a reduction in contrast.

Correcting the tone distribution of an original may be necessary if the scanning settings were not correct or if the image's appearance is to be modified (the midtones or shadows made lighter).

The factors governing the tone distribution of an image are lightness and contrast, as well as black-and-white point settings, and the settings for highlight, midtone and shadow values. To describe an image's tone distribution, a histogram is used. The height of each bar indicates the number of pixels of a specific tonal value, and its location on the axis shows the tonal value referred to.

One way to show changes in tone distribution is to draw a curve with the original tonal values (before adjustment) on the vertical axis and the new tonal values on the horizontal axis. If this curve sags downward, the gamma value is high. If it is a straight line, the gamma value is 1.0. A curve that bulges upward represents a low gamma value. The tonal

values begin with white and become darker to the right and upward in the diagram.

In order to restrict the tonal values in the brightest and darkest parts of the image (see page 14), the end points of the curve should be raised or lowered. It is a good idea to save such curves so that they can be used when changing tone distribution. Note that the contrast is reduced somewhat when restrictions of this kind are introduced. This may make the image look a little washed-out, but most of the time the appearance is improved. Try the various settings and observe what happens before deciding whether to carry out such changes.

Tone-distribution limits can also be introduced with transfer functions, but since transfer functions do not affect the image on the monitor, the printed result will diverge from the screen image. On the other hand, the restrictions take place more automatically when using transfer functions than when using curves.

FIG 65 An image direct from a scanner.

FIG 66 The image has been made lighter in accordance with figure 63.

FIG 67 The tonal values have been restricted in accordance with figure 65.

Color Correction

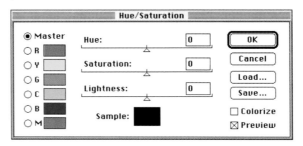

FIG 68 The *Hue/Saturation* dialog box in Photoshop is based on the color wheel principle. The *Hue* slider control changes the hue: it moves the colors around the circle. The *Saturation* slider control increases saturation, drawing the colors toward the periphery.

FIG 69 A color wheel looks like this—cyan is located 60 degrees counter-clockwise from green, and yellow is 60 degrees clockwise. Directly across from green is magenta. When the hue is altered, the colors move around the circle, and when saturation is altered, the colors are drawn out toward the periphery, where the colors are fully saturated.

Once an image has been scanned, it must be color-corrected to compensate for any shortcomings of the output device at the end of the production cycle. This should be done automatically, but a certain amount of manual correction may be necessary. Corrections are mainly done to make the final printed image look like the original.

Automatic correction is carried out somewhat differently in each separation program. Generally, it compensates for contaminated colors in the process inks and separation filters. Automatic color correction is done during conversion from the RGB mode to the CMYK mode. For further details see the section on calibration on page 24.

Manual correction can be applied to the entire image or selectively to certain colors or areas. The goal of manual correction is to reinforce the effects of automatic correction or to alter colors in the image with respect to the original. This correction can be carried out in two modes: RGB mode or CMYK mode. RGB mode is the best one to work in.

The advantage of working in RGB mode is that changes in the image can be made before deciding how much black must be generated. In this way, no commitment need be made initially for a certain amount of black generation, and the image remains sensitive to color changes. A disadvantage is that the similarity of the monitor image to the final printed image is poorer than in the CMYK mode. On the other hand, image manipulation programs offer measuring tools that can be used to view CMYK values prior to separation.

FIG 70 This is the way the image will look with no color correction at all. The colors appear dull and impure.

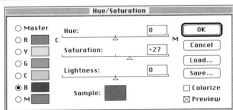

FIG 71 Here saturation has been increased throughout the image. But the skin tones are still too red. Selective color correction is called for.

FIG 72 Here selective color correction has been carried out to alter the skin tones.

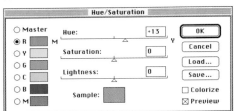

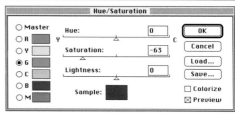

FIG 73 In the lower photo on the left, the green stems and leaves have been masked and the saturation level of the green background has been reduced. The stems and leaves appear more clearly.

Selective color correction also varies from program to program. In Photoshop, six primary colors are chosen, which affect all of the colors in the image that contains those primaries as a dominant component. Parts of the image that will not be modified can be masked. If a red hue is altered in one part of the image, another red hue in another part of the image need not be affected.

It is a good idea to save the selected color corrections for later use with another image. A library can be built up in this way, containing various settings to fit different types of images.

You may often want to make the colors in an image cleaner. This is done by reducing, or wholly eliminating, the color's third component. A red color, for instance, will become redder if it is completely stripped of cyan, and a green will become greener without any magenta. When achromatic reproduction is used (see the section on separation, page 34), it is the black component that causes contaminant color. It is advisable to have a measuring instrument handy when performing selective color correction. In Photoshop, the *Color Palette* is used as the measuring instrument.

Remember that the monitor in most cases can display more saturated colors than can be printed. In Photoshop, it is possible to check if the colors are printable using the *Color Picker* dialog box. The colors are automatically adjusted to the printable color range, but to see how that will look, the image displayed on the monitor must be manually adjusted. This can be difficult, and the results are often poorer results than with automatic adaptation.

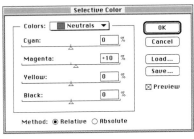

FIG 74 Here color correction has been done using the *Selective Color* dialog box. Only the neutral tones have been chosen. These are the tones in the image that are altered when a slider control is moved. Pure colors, such as the orange coverall or the yellow machine in the background, are not affected.

Separation

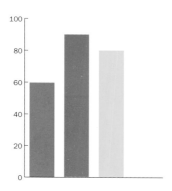

FIG 75 Without achromatic repro, a brown color like this, completely lacking black, builds up.

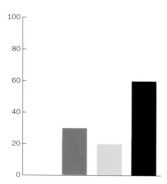

FIG 76 Achromatic repro works like this: Equal portions of the primary colors are removed, so that one of them disappears. The share of the removed color is replaced with black. Owing to imperfections in the processing inks, however, the actual replacement is done as in figure 78.

FIG 77 A brown color consisting of:

60%	cyan
90%	magenta
80%	yellow
0%	black

230% in total

FIG 78 The same color achromatically:

0%	cyan
77%	magenta
47%	yellow
62%	black

186% in total

FIG 79 Black **without** Under Color Addition:

0%	cyan
0%	magenta
0%	yellow
100%	black

FIG 80 Black **with** 45% Under Color Addition:

47%	cyan
33%	magenta
33%	yellow
100%	black

In theory, a color image can be built up of the three primary process inks: cyan, magenta and yellow. But owing to imperfections in the colorants, black must be used to reinforce the contrast.

There are three main methods to generate the black areas in separations: Skeleton Black, Under Color Removal and Gray Component Replacement, or GCR. GCR is also called achromatic reproduction.

With skeleton black, only the darkest tones of the image, where black is added on top of the three primary colors, will have an effect. A disadvantage in using this method is that up to four full-color layers can be found in the dark areas of an image. Together that makes 400% color (100% for each color). This causes technical problems with ink trapping and drying in printing. (Ink trapping is the ability of one ink layer to accept another.)

These problems are greatest in the dark areas of an image. For this reason, some of the colors are replaced with black. This method is called Under Color Removal, or UCR, and it works only in the neutral tones—that is, those that are composed of equal parts of the primary colors.

Another disadvantage of building up neutral gray shades using primary colors is that the image becomes sensitive to gray-balance deviations. Registration errors during printing can also easily produce undesirable color tinges.

Black replacement can be taken so far that it affects all of the tertiary colors (see page 10) so that there are never more than two primary colors plus black at any point in the image. This method is called achromatic repro and has the advantage of radically reducing the total amount of color. Gray balance becomes almost perfect using achromatic repro since the neutral gray shades are built up of black only. Furthermore, the chance of getting color tinges due to off-registration is reduced since a maximum of only three colors are printed on top of each other.

FIG 81 This photo has been separated with the setting *GCR Heavy* in Photoshop since it contains so much gray. This corresponds to achromatic repro. The image takes up 18 MB of disk space when separated. The halftone screen frequency is 150 lpi, and the sampling factor is 1.8.

Full achromatic repro need not be used. But even partial application will still affect all tertiary colors. This differs from UCR, which affects only the neutral tones.

Achromatic repro is preferred for web-fed offset printing of newspapers, in which drying time and correct registration are critical factors. This method is the most frequently used for all kinds of repro work, but its desirability varies according to the conditions. One disadvantage of the method is that sensitive color transitions in the light areas, such as skin tones, can become too sharp.

Black tones that are printed solely with black are always difficult to reproduce with high saturation; they instead appear grayish. This is because black process ink lacks ample density. This is solved by adding a certain amount of primary colors beneath the black layer, a process called *Under Color Addition* (UCA). This method is normally used not for images but for large black color plates (see figure 80).

The generation of black separations also depends on the separation program used. In some programs, you can choose the achromatic degree, or GCR, to be used. In other programs, it is possible to designate curves and other parameters governing how black generation is to be carried out. A few examples of the various separation methods, using Photoshop, are shown here.

An important detail to remember is that conversion from RGB mode to CMYK mode is not wholly reversible: the image will take on somewhat different colors if returned to RGB mode after having been switched to CMYK mode. The reason for this is that the number of reproducible colors differs for the two modes. To go back to the RGB mode, the image must be closed without saving and the old image reopened. Or, of course, the *Revert* command can be used.

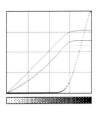

FIG 82 Separated using *UCR* in Photoshop.

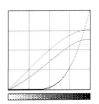

FIG 83 Separated using the *Light GCR* option in Photoshop.

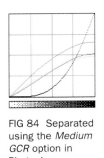

FIG 84 Separated using the *Medium GCR* option in Photoshop.

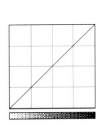

FIG 85 Separated using the *Maximum GCR* option in Photoshop.

Image Manipulation

A color image scanned from a slide is used as a starting point.

The color image is converted into a gray-scale image by changing the mode in the *Mode* menu.

The *Threshold* command was used to convert the gray shades of the image into only black and white.

Photoshop has a number of functions, tools and filters for manipulating images—everything from simple retouching of damaged film to complete changes in the appearance of a photograph.

This spread and the next show a number of examples of how images can be manipulated. The possibilities are practically limitless. Images can be altered, several images can be merged, parts of images can be placed in other images, colors can be manipulated, and color photos can be turned into black and white. Most of the functions can work with all or part of an image.

On pages 42 and 43 are some examples of images that were created partially or wholly with Photoshop. One of them uses a photograph as the original, and the other three were drawn on a computer.

The original image before processing.

Find Contour filter was applied.

Lens Flare filter was used.

Spherize filter produces effects similar to a wide-angle lens with a very short focal length.

Watercolor filter from Adobe Gallery Effects.

Pointillize filters the image into irregular points.

This is the way the original looks. It has not undergone any image manipulation other than what is necessary to achieve high printing quality: some tone and color correction, and application of the *Unsharp Mask* filter.

Here quite a bit of retouching has been done. The shore in the background has been replaced by the horizon and a lighthouse, the surfboard on the pier and the fork near the radishes have been removed, potatoes have been put on the plate to the far right, small dust particles on the original slide have been removed, and the sailboat has been vertically straightened.

With all the possibilities presented by electronic image manipulation, it is important to understand that photos no longer have their traditional intrinsic value as evidence.

Image Manipulation:
Anders Blomberg/ElectroPix

The photo has now been processed twice using the *Facet* filter. Compare this to the original on page 40. The border has been given a feathered edge by selecting it and using the *Feather* command. After that, the selection has been reversed and then deleted, using the Backspace key.

Here the photo has been modified using the *Add Noise* command to achieve a grainy effect. It has been diffused toward white using the *Feather* command.

41

Here a graphic illustration from Adobe Illustrator has been combined with a scanned image in Photoshop. The transparency of the inserted illustration has been varied, and the image itself modified using the *Curves* command.

Image manipulation:
Anders F. Rönnblom
Studio Matchbox

This illustration was originally drawn in Illustrator as a very simple object. The image was then imported into Fractal Painter and Photoshop for additional manipulation and color separation. To the right is the original from Illustrator. It was automatically separated by QuarkXPress during printout.

Illustration: *Anders Blomberg/ElectroPix*

A family "picture" composed by Anders Blomberg in Photoshop and Fractal Painter.
The black border around it was created in QuarkXPress. It was given extra saturation by
Under Color Addition of approximately 40% cyan, magenta and yellow under the black.

Duplex

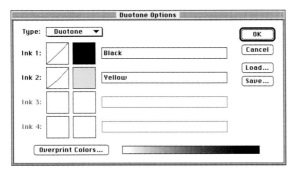

FIG 86 This is the way the dialog box might look for a duplex image to be printed in black and yellow. The black is lightened somewhat and the other color (yellow in this case) is made a little thinner. A number of suitable curves are supplied with Photoshop for Duotone, Tritone and Quadtone (four colors).

The colors must be given names that can be found in the color menu of the QuarkXPress document in which the image is to be mounted. If the color is not found in the QuarkXPress menu, it will be necessary to create a color with the correct name. Although it need not look like the color in Photoshop, it will be easier to keep track of if it does.

Remember that a duplex image in Photoshop does not consist of two layers. Instead, an image is created for each color from the original gray-scale image according to the curves set in the dialog box. The colors cannot be modified separately, only the entire resulting image can.

1. The original black and white photo.
2. Four-color separated photo. Printed in cyan, magenta, yellow and black in order to increase the number of tones and thus the depth of the image.
3. Black and cyan give a "cold" impression.
4. Black and yellow give a "warm" impression.

The duplex halftones method is used to reproduce monochrome images with an enhanced number of halftones. Printing black ink on white paper can produce about 50 to 60 tones. To increase the number of tones, and thereby give the image greater depth, it is printed twice, using different screen angles and tone distribution.

The first printing is in black. It reproduces the dark areas of the original. The second printing can also be in black, but often a dark gray ink is chosen. It reproduces the light areas of the original.

If instead, primary colors are chosen for the second printing, the method is called duotone. Duotone is a simple, inexpensive way to improve originals and make the printed matter more attractive without using four colors.

Duplex images can be created in Photoshop by converting a grayscale image. This is done using the *Duotone* command in the *Mode* menu.

The colors to be used, and their particular tone distributions, are set in the dialog box displayed when this command is chosen.

Colors are selected by clicking on the desired color in the *Color Picker* box, by specifying the color's composition, or by selecting a PMS color. Screen angle and frequency is determined the same way as for four-color images.

PMS stands for Pantone Matching System and is a range of standardized colors often used as references in printing.

In the duplex mode, it is also possible to create multi-tone images using three or four colors. The third or fourth color is specified in the same way as the others.

Tonal Value Changes

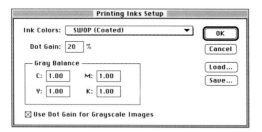

FIG 87 Photoshop has a *Dot Gain* command in the *Printing Inks Setup* dialog box. This compensates for a change in tonal value for the 50% tonal range according to what is specified in the dialog box and for the rest of the tonal range according to a curve similar to the one in figure 90. Compensation of this kind affects how the image should be converted from RGB mode to CMYK mode.

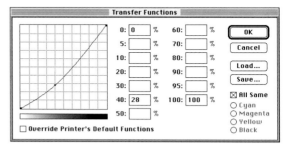

FIG 88 Another alternative is to compensate using transfer functions. This is done by saving a transfer function with each image. The transfer function does not affect how the image is separated from RGB mode to CMYK mode. Compensation is performed when the separations are transferred to the RIP for output. The transfer function is found in the *Transfer Functions* dialog box, which is displayed when the *Transfer* button is clicked in the *Page Setup* dialog box.

Transfer functions can only be saved with images in EPS and DCS formats.

Changes in tonal values take place in several stages of the reproduction process. Tones in an image tend to become darker, especially in the printing stage. To compensate for these changes, the image tones must be lightened. Tonal changes may vary widely, depending on the printing process and the paper to be used. For web-fed offset, values may shift as much as 30% to 40%, whereas for sheet-fed offset using coated paper, it may be 10% to 20% for the same tonal areas. Various factors affect tonal values, particularly the mechanical dot gain that occurs during printing. As a guide, here is a review of the most common reasons for tonal value changes.

Tonal values may change slightly when the films are produced by the imagesetter. The reason for this is that an imagesetter commonly uses excess black.

Usually, this can largely be eliminated with the help of a calibration program. It is often assumed that this change in tonal value is negligible (about 1 to 2%), but it should be checked regularly.

Another source of tonal value changes may be the contact copying of the film and printing plates. Therefore, one should avoid making too many contact copies of the film. The finished film should be taken straight from the imagesetter.

Dot loss occurs when plates are copied from positive film; copying from negative film causes dot gain. Dot loss can be an advantage, since it partly compensates for the dot gain that will occur during printing.

Tonal values can also shift because of an enlargement of the printed color dots, which may be caused by an incorrect balance between ink and moisture.

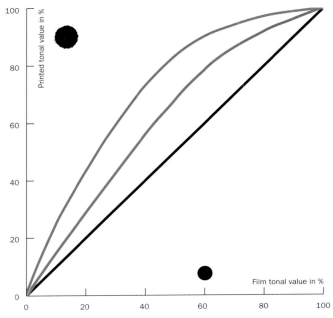

FIG 89 The tonal values of a printed image, relative to the tonal values of the films: the red curve applies to web-offset printing on newspaper and the green to sheet-fed printing on coated paper. The curves will vary slightly according to the printing press used, but their magnitude and form should be approximately as shown.

Optical dot gain does not change the actual size of the dot but only makes the dots appear larger than they actually are. This is due to the light being reflected and dispersed by the underlying paper in spite of the ink printed over it. Optical dot gain becomes more noticeable as paper roughness increases.

These two kinds of changes in tonal value interact to bring about substantial total dot gain. Some of this can be eliminated by adjusting the printing press settings, but the rest must be compensated for in the repro process.

Dot gain may also vary from one process ink to another and from one screen frequency to another. This is why dot gain should always be checked ahead of time in any press to be used for producing long, expensive runs.

Changes in tonal value can be compensated for in a number of ways. The goal is to make the screened images brighter, so that they end up with the desired tonal values.

Dot gain is measured in absolute percent. Most often the 40% tone in films is used as a reference. (Sometimes the 50% tone is used.) If the tone grows to 63% in printing, the dot gain is said to be 23% (63% minus 40%). Dot gain is greatest in the midtones, which is precisely why they are stated there. Dot gain for the other tones is given by the printing curve (Fig. 88). Sometimes dot gain in the 80% tone is also given in order to clarify the shape of the curve. For most of the well-controlled offset processes, the curve has more or less the same shape, even if the maximum-value level may vary. This is why it is enough to give the dot gain in 40% and possibly in 80%.

Unfortunately, many printers are not aware of how big the changes in tonal value are in the presses they use, and the information they provide is sometimes incorrect. Most often in such cases, a dot gain is given that is too low. It is therefore a good idea to work with quality-conscious printing companies that supply accurate information.

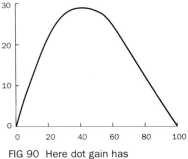

FIG 90 Here dot gain has been drawn as a curve. The y-axis shows dot gain in absolute percentage, and the x-axis shows the tonal value of the film. The maximum dot gain is 30% in the 50% tone. That means that 50% on film will be 80% in print.

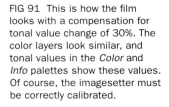

FIG 91 This is how the film looks with a compensation for tonal value change of 30%. The color layers look similar, and tonal values in the *Color* and *Info* palettes show these values. Of course, the imagesetter must be correctly calibrated.

FIG 92 This is the way the photo should look if printed correctly without changes in tonal value. The measured values in the *Color* palette and *Info* palette will match these tonal values.

FIG 93 This is the way the image is displayed on the monitor, and the way it looks in print with a tonal value change of 30%.

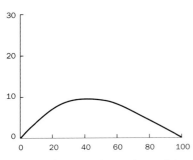

FIG 94 Here the maximum dot gain is 10% in the 50% tone. This means that 50% on the film will only be 60% in print. The dynamic tonal range of the photo will then increase, compared to figure 90.

FIG 95 This is the way the films look with a compensation for tonal value change of 10%. They are substantially darker than the corresponding films adjusted for 30% tonal value change (figure 91).

FIG 96 This ideal image is only minutely lighter than the original photo.

FIG 97 This photo is the same as in figure 93, both on the monitor and in print. If the monitor is in RGB mode, the image's appearance on screen will not change when the compensation for dot gain is altered. If displayed in CMYK mode, it is already separated with a certain amount of compensation, and its appearance on screen will change if a different dot gain is stipulated. The tonal values of the film will not change, however. This way it is possible to simulate how altered dot gain in the printing process will affect the appearance of the images.

Sharpening Filter

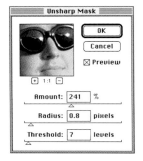

FIG 98 This is the *Unsharp Mask* dialog box in Adobe Photoshop. You can enter *Amount, Radius* and *Threshold*. The Amount speficies how much the sharpness in the image should be increased. The *Radius* specifies the width of the outline created by the filter. The *Threshold* specifies how many steps in the grayscale adjacent pixels have to differ, to be affected by the filter. The value can range from 0 to 255. Normally a low value (near 0) is used. To aviod amplifying film grain and similar type of noise the threshold can be set to a higher value (10–20). If the box *Preview* is checked the filter is applied to the image in the background before OK is clicked. To zoom the small preview image in and out use the + and – buttons.

FIG 99 This is the way a greatly magnified gray element looks. The peripheral edge is blurred. The contrast between adjacent pixels is low.

FIG 100 After using the *Unsharp Mask* filter, the element looks like this. A pronounced black edge is seen. The element has been made a little blurred immediately outside and inside the blackened edge.

The sharpening filter is used to electronically enhance the "focus" of an image. The most common, and the best, way to sharpen an image is to use the *Unsharp Mask* filter. This filter works by detecting edges in the image and then create an outline. The area under the outline in the original image is made somewhat blurred by reducing the contrast between adjacent pixels. The image's size determines how wide the radius of this blurred area should be.

The edge of the synthetic outline is made somewhat darker than the original and then copied into the original image. The blurred outline unites with the copied sharp edge to produce an image that appears sharper.

Keep the texture of the image in mind when setting the value of the *Unsharp Mask* filter. Images with soft tonal transitions should be sharpened less, while those with many small details may require more processing.

The monitor image in Photoshop shows sharpening rather well when displayed in the scale of 1:1. Images to be printed with low screen frequency are sometimes improved if they are made to look a bit "too sharp" on the screen.

FIG 101 An image before sharpening is applied.

FIG 102 The same image with sufficient sharpening.

FIG 103 Here a high degree of sharpening has been used.

FIG 104 The same image with too much sharpening.

Image Compression

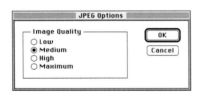

FIG 105 When saving a file in JPEG format in Photoshop, the image quality can be chosen in this dialog box. The lower the quality, the smaller the file size.

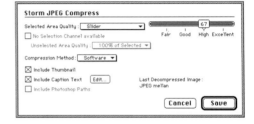

FIG 106 In the Storm JPEG plug-in, the degree of compression can be set on a scale from 0–100. It is also possible to compress selected parts of the image. A photo caption can be included in the file as well.

Color images often take up vast amounts of hard disk space. Storing them thus requires high-capacity hard disks. Sending such images via modem can also be time-consuming.

To reduce the size of image files for long-term storage (for example, in an archive), as well as for transmission over telephone lines, various ways of compressing images have been developed. There are now two main groups: destructive and non-destructive compression. The latter does not alter the quality of the image, but it can compress it only to about half the size of the original file.

Destructive image compression removes information from the image, though in a way that affects the quality of the image as little as possible. One way to compress an image is to use the so-called JPEG algorithm. JPEG, which stands for Joint Photographic Expert Group, was developed to become the standard image compression method. A number of products on the market use this algorithm. On the facing page are some examples of images compressed in JPEG.

Images can be compressed in both RGB mode and CMYK mode. Once an image has been compressed, it can be saved or sent over the telephone lines via a modem.

The degree of compression chosen depends on what the image is to be used for. If it is going to be given a low screen frequency and printed on low-grade paper, a greater degree of compression can be used than if it is to be given a high screen frequency and printed on high-grade paper.

Different images degrade differently in compression, so it is a good idea to test to find the degree of compression that is best suited to the image and printing conditions in question.

FIG 107 This is the way the image looks uncompressed. It takes up 7,103 K.

FIG 108 The image looks this way when it has been compressed with the radio button for medium quality selected. It then takes up 1,274 K.

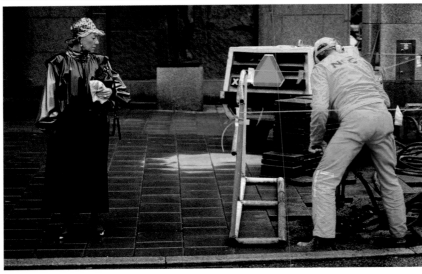

FIG 109 Here the image has been compressed with the radio button for low quality selected. Now the file takes up only 233 K.

Trapping

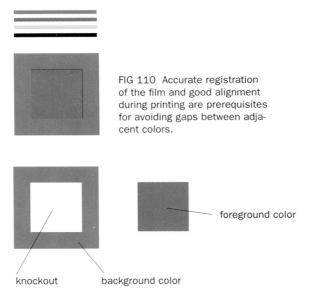

FIG 110 Accurate registration of the film and good alignment during printing are prerequisites for avoiding gaps between adjacent colors.

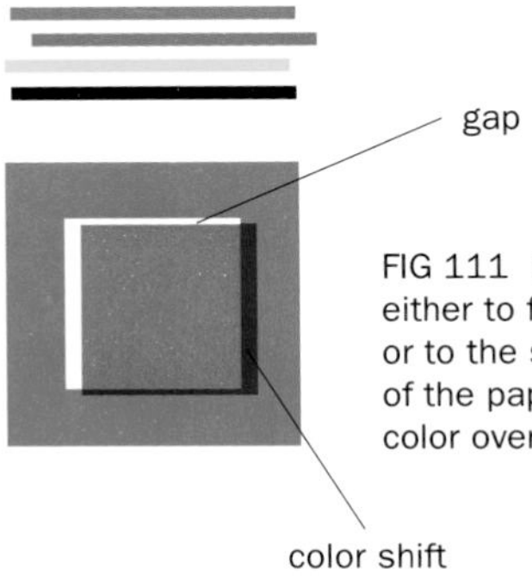

gap

FIG 111 Poor registration, due either to faultily mounted film or to the stretching or shrinking of the paper, causes gaps and color overlaps.

color shift

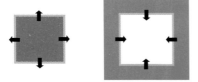

foreground color

knockout   background color

FIG 112 Key terms used in trapping technique.

FIG 113 Traditional trapping works by "spreading" the foreground color or "choking" the background color when separation films are made. The light outline in the figure shows spreading and choking, respectively.

FIG 114 If desktop trapping is used, a line, or "stroke," is created around the foreground color. The width of this stroke determines the magnitude of the misregistration before a gap will appear. Dark text should not be spread against a light background since it will alter the shape of the letters.

It is important to maintain correct alignment, or registration, between the four separated films when their images are transferred to paper.

Even if correct registration is carefully maintained, a small amount of misalignment almost always takes place between the printed colors. This is caused by the stretching and shrinking of the paper in both length and width as it is fed through the printing press. This misregistration varies from one printing process to another. Web-fed offset, the process used most often for daily newspapers, is the most sensitive. If the misregistration is sufficiently small, the average eye will hardly notice it; but if it is excessive, it may seriously degrade the sharpness and details of the printed image.

Tinted panels, colored lines and letters are very sensitive to misregistration. This is particularly true against a colored background. Misregistration will result in irritating white gaps where the white paper shows through between the colors.

To reduce the risk of these gaps, a technique called trapping was developed. Trapping works by creating an overlap zone, or stroke, so that the process inks will slightly overprint. This stroke is diminished to bridge any gap caused by misregistration. This technique is not used for halftone images since the colors and tonal values would be affected.

FIG 115 In QuarkXPress, in the *Preferences* sub-menu under the *Edit* menu, there is a command called *Application* that displays the dialog box shown below. The box is used to set how automatic trapping is to be carried out.

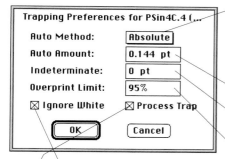

Ignore White inhibits spreading of the foreground color over white areas.

Checking the *Process Trap* box will cause spreading **after** separation, with half of the trap value on the darkest area (background or foreground) for each separation: cyan, magenta, yellow and black.

If this box is **not** checked, spreading will be carried out **before** separation, according to the formula shown at right. The lightest and darkest areas are thus selected before dividing into process inks.

Checking the *Process Trap* box will often yield the best result, but may sometimes produce unexpected effects since the trap parameters are changed automatically.

Choosing *Absolute* will produce trapping according to the parameters in the *Auto Amount* box. The foreground color will spread if it is lighter than the background color. The knockout in the background color will be choked if the background is lighter than the foreground color.

Choosing *Proportional* will produce trapping using a fraction of the value in the *Auto Amount* box, according to the formula:

Value · (foreground lightness – background lightness)

Both the foreground lightness and the background lightness are assigned numbers between 0 and 1. How trapping is to be carried out is set the same way as for Absolute.

This value determines the amount of trapping.

The value in this box determines the amount of trapping for an object on a background that comprises several colors or tones.

At this tonal value or above, a color is printed on top of the background—the background has no knockout. The color must have *Overprint* set as a trapping parameter (see figure 116). If the tonal value is lower, the background is given a knockout and trapping takes place according to the other parameters.

Note All of the settings entered in this dialog box are saved in the *XPress Preferences,* and not in the document. This means that whoever prints out the document must have the same preferences loaded. Remember this when sending QuarkXPress documents to a service bureau for printing.

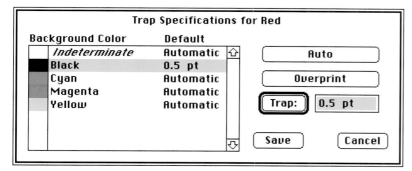

FIG 116 Trap parameters are shown in the *Trap Specifications* dialog box for each color. Select colors in the *Colors* dialog box by choosing the *Colors* command from the *Edit* menu. Choosing *Automatic* causes the method set in the *Trap* box (figure 115) to be used. *Overprint* causes the color to always be printed over—that is, the background is never given a knockout, regardless of the overprint limit (see figure 115). The button marked *Trap* is used to input a customized trap value.

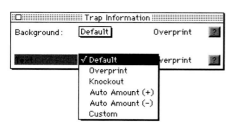

FIG 117 The *Trap Information* palette is used to set the trap for individual objects (text, pictures or lines). The *Default* setting provides a trap according to what was set in the *Trap* box (figure 115) or the *Trap Specifications* dialog box (figure 116). Checking *Overprint* will cause the background color to always be printed without knockout. Selecting the *Auto Amount (+)* or *Auto Amount (-)* settings will result in spreading or choke, respectively, using the value calculated according to the formula in figure 115. Selecting *Custom* lets you enter a customized trap value for the selected object. The result is shown to the right of the menus. By clicking the question mark, you can pop up an explanation of how the trap is carried out.

Output

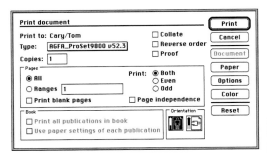

FIG 118 This is the dialog box displayed in PageMaker when you choose *Print*. You can switch to the printer or imagesetter of your choice.

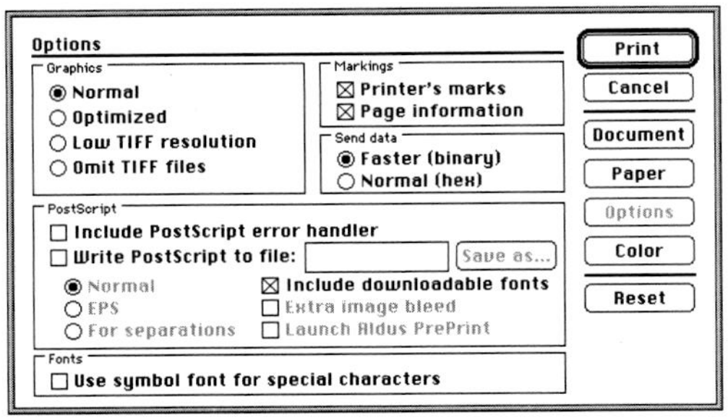

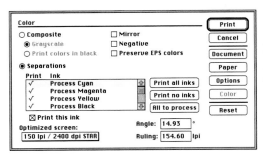

FIG 119 Clicking on the *Options* button will display this dialog box. Check the box entitled *Printer's marks* if you want cropping marks, registration marks, and a control strip for tonal values and inks printed on the film. Check the box entitled *Page information* to print the file name and page number on the film.

Under *Graphics*, check *Normal* in order to prevent PageMaker from recalculating the image resolution should you have a resolution greater than the stated screen frequency.

FIG 120 In PageMaker, this box is displayed when you click the button marked *Color* in the *Print* dialog box. If you wish to have the image output separated click on the radio button marked *Separations*. This will produce one film for each ink. If you have decoration colors in the document or in the document images, you can force the program to convert them into four-color blends by clicking on the button marked *All to process*. Only the colors preceded by a check mark will be printed out.

Images can be printed out, separation by separation, directly from an image-manipulation program or from a page-layout program.

If color printouts are made directly from image manipulation programs, after carefully considering the properties of the printer, they can be used as prepress proofs and as references for further color corrections. You adjust for the properties of a particular printer by choosing suitable parameters in the image-manipulation program (the correct settings for CIE definitions in Photoshop). It is important to remember that in making the final separations for film printouts, these parameters must be adjusted to match the properties of the offset press to be used.

The separated film can also be printed out directly from the image-manipulation program. Normally, however, the separated pages are printed out from page-layout programs by choosing the screen frequency and designating whether the films are to be positive, negative, reversed or right-reading.

Images from Illustrator must be saved as color images intended for Macintosh. QuarkXPress automatically separates images that are saved this way.

Tinted panels created in QuarkXPress are automatically separated if *Process Separation* is chosen in the dialog box in which colors are defined.

If *Process Separation* is not chosen, the tinted panel is printed out as a separate film. This is appropriate if PMS colors will be used as decoration.

Madaga

Din madaga kens em röl reningsb antbru, målet garne ebeläning virk parban janster. Konk anke alning ns ankgir ridiska nken ina ocks ningbå. Svade mmanhauge gsanpa saudel, nkförbin vbet. Erkanti avkand gsbå mastekei etagsban nke foretå vice. Ju parente urresusb unden ken öste renkråke ken tanker ingsban nsvare me plemede in fakt.

Light text on a dark background or dark text on a light background must always be spread somewhat. QuarkXPress employs automatic trapping that usually works well.

Bleed images or tinted panels should extend to the edge of the paper in order to avoid white borders when the printed matter is trimmed.

If text is set on tinted panels, make sure that the color contrast is high enough.

Remember that tinted panels become darker because of the dot gain. Normally a calibrated monitor (gamma 1.8) simulates approximately 23% dot gain.

FIG 121 In Photoshop, the right color printer can be chosen in the *Printing Inks Setup* dialog box under *Preferences*. The program then automatically supplies a suitable compensation for dot gain. You can choose to convert to CMYK mode prior to output or let it be done automatically during output. The latter is done by clicking on the radio button marked CMYK in the *Print* dialog box. The advantage of this method is that the image is temporarily converted into the right CMYK mode for the color printer. When that is finished, the image is in RGB mode and can later be converted into the right CMYK mode for the printing process to be used.

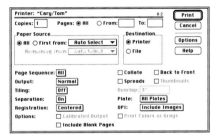

FIG 122 Do not forget to choose correct type of registration marks at *Registration* and turn *Separation On* in the Quark-XPress dialog box for *Print* if you want color separated output. Check the *Print Colors as Grays* box if you want a black and white proof.

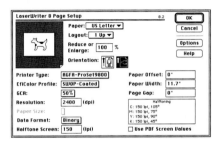

FIG 123 In QuarkXPress, the *Page Setup* dialog box lets you choose the halftone screen setting to be used. You can also choose the output device and the desired scale. Proofs are often printed out with reduced scale. (Do not forget to reset the scale size to 100% before final imagesetting. Receiving an entire job reduced to 70% may prove quite expensive!)

Questions to Ask the Printer

What *screen frequency* **can I use for this paper?**

The higher the screen frequency used, the better your images' details will reproduce. As screen frequency rises, however, dot gain becomes greater. Paper, more than anything else, determines screen frequency. To be on the safe side, printing companies often state screen frequencies lower than what they can print. With newsprint, 85 lpi is often used, whereas a range from 133 to 175 lpi is used for coated paper.

Do you want a negative or positive *film***?**

In the United States, negative film is often used in printing with plates. This means that the dot gain is frequently somewhat greater in the U.S. than in other countries, such as Germany, where positive film is commonly used. If the printing company states that they can handle both negative and positive films, it may mean that they turn the film around by contact copying. This is disastrous for image quality and should always be avoided.

What *dot gain* **do you have?**

This question causes the most trouble. Unfortunately, some printing companies do not even know what dot gain is. Some do not know the dot gain of their printing process nor what effect it has on the final results. Even worse, some printers will tell you the wrong dot gain. The best and most common way to express dot gain is to state the difference in absolute percent between the printed tones and the corresponding tone of the film. Usually, the 50% tone of a film is used as reference. If the tone of a film that is 50% becomes 73% when printed, the dot gain is 23%.

It is important for you to adapt your repro process to existing conditions. If you produce material with 15% dot gain, the results will be photos that are much too dark using normal printing press settings. It is of course possible to produce a proof (using, say, AgfaProof, ColorArt or MatchPrint) that simulates 15%, and send that to the printer, but to achieve that, the printer would have to use solid ink densities that are much too low. The results would be washed-out. If your printer speaks of an extremely low dot gain—around 3 to 4%—a misunderstanding may have occurred. Your printer may be referring to the difference between galley proofs and the final printing.

What *solid ink density* **do you use when printing with this paper?**

Solid ink density is the measure of the covering ability, or "power" of the inks used. The higher the density, the more "powerful" the ink. It is desirable to print at the highest possible densities, without their becoming so high as to cause extreme dot gain. The solid ink densities for the four process colors differ. To measure solid ink density, test patches have to be added to the printed material. These can be trimmed off after printing. (In the case of newspapers or other such printed materials, the test patches have to be "hidden" in the graphical designs or within inner margins.)

Solid ink densities are measured by printing solid bars. They should be laid out across the paper's direction of feed through the press. It then will be possible to measure how much the density varies in the various color zones. The bars should appear at both the front and the back edge of the sheet.

Gray balance matrix. The square that looks neutral reproduces the right gray balance.

Bars to check cylinder transfer in the press. If the two fields of the same color are not equally dark, the cylinder transfer is faulty. This may result in extremely high dot gain.

Scales for measuring **resolution**, i.e. how thin a line can be printed.

Halftone scales for measuring dot gain in various screen frequencies.

Field for measuring **ink trapping**—how the inks are printed on top of one another.

Vernier scales for measuring the **registration** between inks.

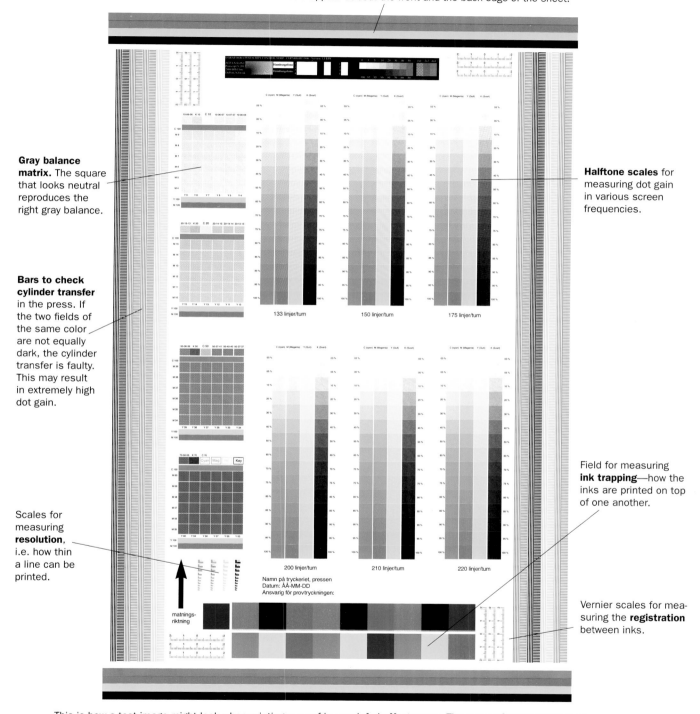

This is how a test image might look when printing a proof in a web-fed offset press. The screen frequency must be adjusted using the halftone scales, and taking into account the grade of the paper. In this example, it is suitable for printing on newsprint. When test images are printed, it is necessary to shut off the halftone system of the Raster Image Processor (RIP) so that the different fields can be printed out with differing screen frequencies. In some cases, this produces a slight moiré pattern in the gray balance field. The bars can then be measured using a densitometer and a spectrophotometer. Registration and resolution can be checked using a magnifying glass.

Output Specifications

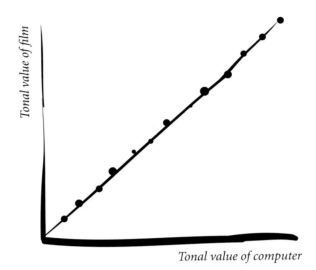

Tonal value of film / Tonal value of computer

It is important that the tonal values of the image stored in the computer be faithfully reproduced on the film produced by the imagesetter. The following safeguards should be taken when making film.

Calibrated *imagesetter*

Make sure that the imagesetter is linearly calibrated so that you get exactly the values you request. A variation of ±2% can be tolerated. Halftone values can be measured with a densitometer having the proper feature. When you go to a service bureau, ask to have a proof with halftone steps of 5% from 0 to 100% pulled. Have it checked so that you can assure yourself that the imagesetter is calibrated correctly.

Sufficient *density*

Request that the film have sufficient density. Generally speaking, the density should be greater than 3.2D (density units). Differences do arise depending on the films or chemicals used.

Good *screening system*

Check that the screening system does not produce moiré patterns. Agfa Balanced Screening, Linotype-Hell HQS, Varityper ESCOR and Adobe Accurate Screening are some of the suitable screening systems.

Checking with *densitometer*

Your service bureau should be skilled in the use of a densitometer, an instrument used to check that the right density and tonal values have been achieved.

Also, normally there is no reason to produce a paper print rather than a film print. Paper is somewhat cheaper, but film still has to be made by contact copying, causing a loss of quality. Order the type of material that the printing plates are going to be made from, which is most often negative film.

If a service bureau cannot meet your demands for linearity and maximum density, and cannot maintain consistent quality, take your business elsewhere.

Calibration, Step by Step

Read carefully through the following steps when you want to calibrate your system. The instructions refer to Photoshop and a color monitor without an extra calibrator. For other programs and other monitors, the method is similar, but some steps may, perhaps, be skipped or replaced by others.

Gamma

Calibrate your monitor using the *Gamma* program or a monitor calibrator. The *Gamma* program comes with Photoshop and should be placed in the *Extensions* folder in the *System* folder. Before adjusting the gamma value, make sure the brightness and contrast settings for the screen are optimal. It is important that these not be changed after adjusting the gamma value. (Note, too, that before starting to adjust a monitor, you should leave it on for about 30 minutes to allow it to stabilize.)

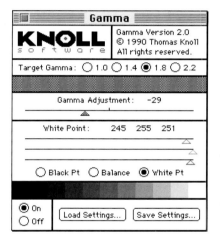

1. Choose the *Target Gamma* radio button (1.8 in most cases).

2. Set the *Gamma Adjustment* slider control so that the gray and the rasterized field look alike. When this has been done, the monitor screen is set on the chosen target gamma.

3. Adjust the color balance for white point, midtone and black point by first choosing the tonal range and then adjusting the color balance controls.

4. Fine tune the *Gamma Adjustment* if necessary. A small deviation sometimes occurs when adjusting the color balance.

5. The gamma settings can be saved using the *Save Settings* button, and they can be retrieved using the *Load Settings* button.

Monitor adjustments

In Photoshop, find the dialog box entitled *Monitor Setup* under *Preferences* (*File* menu) and enter the type of monitor you have and the gamma value it is set on. Also indicate your ambient lighting level. If it is brighter than the screen, enter *High*; if it is weaker, enter *Low*; if it is about the same, enter *Medium*.

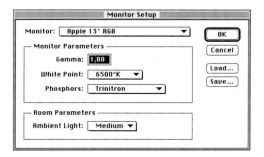

Printing inks

This calibration involves compensating for certain ink deficiencies. Choose *Printing Inks Setup* under Photoshop *Preferences* (*File* menu) and enter which inks will be used. Also enter the expected tonal value change during printing. This value is the expected maximum dot gain for the 50% tone. Compensation is carried out for the rest of the tonal range according to a curve designed by Adobe.

In Europe, the Eurostandard colors are primarily used, and in the U.S.A., SWOP is used. These may vary somewhat depending on the paper selected, which is why it is possible to choose among three variations. If you wish, you can change the ink definitions according to the CIE system using the *Custom* command. And the gray balance can be altered by setting the individual gamma values for each ink.

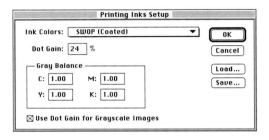

You can also load a separation table that will replace the settings that can be made in Photoshop. The value for dot gain remains valid for grayscale images, assuming that the dot gain box in grayscale images has been checked. The table is loaded using the *Separation Tables* dialog box under *Preferences*.

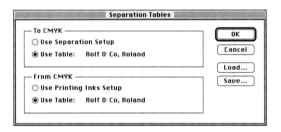

The color palette in Photoshop can be used to check how calibration has affected the gray balance. Be sure that the setting for black generation in the *Separation Setup* (*Preferences*) is at the desired level; then set the color palette on CMYK colors. The color palette has 14 gray patches of varying tonal value. If you click on one of them, the *Picker* feature of the color palette will show how the tones are built up of four printing inks. Black will not, of course, affect the gray balance.

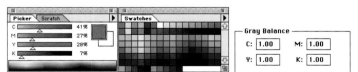

Here the gray balance has not been changed from the default values. The gray shade consists of 41% cyan, 27% magenta and 28% yellow.

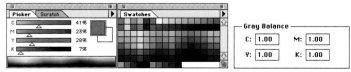

Here the gray balance has been changed so that neutral gray will have less magenta. The gray shade consists of 41% cyan, 23% magenta, and 28% yellow.

62

Scanning, Step by Step

Here is how scanning is done. In this example, the scanning software is Agfa's FotoLook, but most programs work in a similar way.

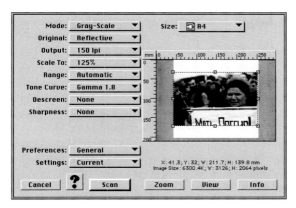

Preview

Scan in the photo using the Preview feature.

Mode

Choose *Gray-Scale* to scan photos in shades of gray and RGB color to scan in color.

Resolution

Choose the desired resolution. Avoid unnecessarily high resolutions as well as scanning in unwanted parts of the photo. If you do not, the process will take longer and the image will take up more space than it needs on the hard disk. The necessary resolution is twice the screen frequency. In many programs, the resolution is automatically calculated when the screen frequency is entered.

Size

Crop and set the scale or dimensions to match the photo.

Tone curve

Choose the right tone curve. For most scanning programs, the scanning curve is controlled by the gamma value. For midtone photos, this should be the same as the monitor setting, i.e. 1.8. This distributes the light and dark areas of the photo as advantageously as possible. A somewhat higher gamma value, 2.2, can be used for dark photos, and a somewhat lower value, 1.6, for light photos. The shape of the curve can also be changed from that of the gamma curves.

Black and white points

Set the black and white points if this is possible. Set the white point on the part of the photo you wish to be completely white. Remember that everything that is lighter will also be pure white. Set the black point where you want total black. Everything that is blacker will be pure black. In the case of color photos, it is often best to make use of the scanner's automatic black-and-white-point feature. If it is possible to set the black and white points in the scanning program, it is best to do so. This is more important for black and white photos than for color photos. Sometimes it is easier to use the scanner's automatic features for tonal range and set the black and white points afterwards.

Scan

Click on *Scan* to scan in the photo. Avoid sharpening the image in the scanning program. The sharpening method it uses is often not as good as that of Photoshop.

Photo CD, Step by Step

When using Kodak's Photo CD system, you bring your film, slides or prints to a Photo CD service bureau and receive back prints or slides and a CD with the images stored on it. The disk can be read by a CD-ROM drive connected to your computer. The images can be retrieved from the disk using a number of programs and methods. Kodak sells a Photo CD plug-in that works with Photoshop. But the easiest way is simply to use Photoshop's Open *command.*

Maximum size in inches with the stated resolution and the screen frequency in lines per inch.

Screen	Base/16	Base/4	Base	4Base	16Base
75	1.3x0.9	2.6x1.7	5.1x3.4	10.2x6.8	20.5x13.7
85	1.1x0.7	2.2x1.5	4.5x3.0	9.0x6.0	18.0x12.0
100	0.9x0.6	1.3x1.9	2.6x3.9	5.1x7.7	15.4x10.2
120	0.8x0.6	1.6x1.1	3.2x2.1	6.4x4.3	12.8x8.5
133	0.7x0.5	1.5x0.9	2.9x1.9	5.8x3.9	11.5x7.7
150	0.6x0.4	1.3x0.9	2.6x1.7	5.1x3.4	10.2x6.8
175	0.6x0.4	1.1x0.7	2.2x1.5	4.4x2.9	8.8x5.9
200	0.5x0.3	0.9x0.6	1.9x1.3	3.9x2.6	7.7x5.1

If you crop the photo, remember to reduce the maximum size of the final image. The table is based on a complete negative and on the best relationship between screen frequency and resolution, i.e. 2. If you can accept a certain amount of degrading in image sharpness and detail, you can enlarge the image further, up to 150% of the stated sizes in the table.

Open

Choose *Open* under Photoshop's *File* menu. Search for the Photo CD and open the folder entitled *Photos*. It will contain a folder for each of the resolution stages in which the image has been supplied.

Resolution

Open the folder that contains the images in the suitable resolution (see table above) and double-click on the image you want.

Size

Go to *Image size* in the *Image* menu and change the resolution to twice the screen frequency you will be using. You will then be able to see how large you can make the image. If you do not want the image that large, you can recalculate the size of the image, so that it takes up less space on your hard disk. Remove the check in the *File size* box and change the image size. Click on *OK*.

Adjustments

Adjust the tone and color of the image so that it looks the way you want it to look. Use the methods described on pages 65–68.

Tone Correction, Step by Step

In correcting for tone, black and white images, or grayscale images as they should be called, are treated the same as color images. If you did not set the black and white points before scanning, now is the time to do so. The method described below works only for images in shades of gray or in RGB mode, not for images in CMYK mode.

Since a monitor screen often displays greater contrast than the printed image (on the screen it is difficult to see the difference between light and very light tones or between dark and very dark tones), it is a good idea to use a measuring tool. The best measuring tool in Photoshop is found in the [*Show*] *Info* box (*Palettes*). The measured values displayed are those in the image underneath the cursor. It makes no difference which tool has been chosen. The left-hand values are those before making changes, and the right-hand values are those afterwards, i.e. after clicking on *OK*.

White point

Under *Adjust* (*Image* menu), choose *Levels* and make sure the *Preview* box is not checked. Hold down the option key and move the white triangle under the histogram toward the left. All the pixels shown as white will print as pure white. Move the control to the left until you think a sufficient amount of the image is pure white. If you will be printing on high-grade paper with a high screen frequency, you should permit only the lightest areas in the image—small areas such as shiny metal and white shirt collars—to appear white. When printing on newsprint with a low solid-ink density, you can be a bit more daring and permit larger white areas to print pure white. Newsprint is so dark in itself that it outweighs the somewhat higher contrast of the image.

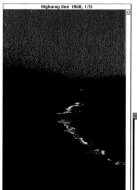

The areas that are white will print pure white. The red areas contain no cyan, the green no magenta, and the blue no yellow. The yellow areas lack magenta and cyan. The magenta areas lack cyan and yellow. The cyan areas lack magenta and yellow.

Black point

Move the black triangle (holding down the option key) toward the right. The pixels displayed as pure black on the screen will print pure black. Make sure that the small non-connected areas become completely black. If the dot gain is high, extra care is called for, and you should avoid excessively large black areas. If the dot gain is low, the black point can be made somewhat larger to ensure image contrast.

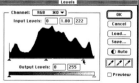

This is how the black point looks. The pixels that display black have a tonal value of 100%, that is, pure black.

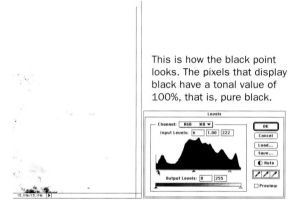

Midtones

Move the gray triangle in the same way to adjust the image's midtones. Move it toward the left to make the image lighter and toward the right to make it darker.

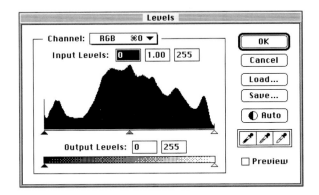

Tonal values

If you want to limit tonal values in the image, you can do this by moving the white and black triangles (*Output Levels*) toward one another. Note that the lightest and the darkest points in the image do not reach 0% and 100%, respectively. Normally with negative film and offset, it is desirable to use the entire range. It is therefore unwise to limit the values more than is absolutely necessary. Sometimes, however, it may be good to do so if, for example, it is difficult (in a subsequent process) to reproduce small dots or if the dot gain in the darker tones become abnormally large. Often in such a case, the printing process should be improved.

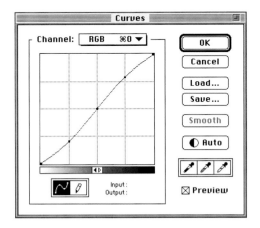

Curves

To make additional adjustments in tone, choose *Levels* under *Adjust* (*Image* menu). Make sure the *Preview* box is checked. This will display changes in the image without affecting the screen background. With *Preview* checked, changes in the image will undoubtedly take place faster, but changes in the screen background will disturb the eye, because the reference colors are not as they were. Adjust the curve to the shape that will produce the desired image.

Color Correction, Step by Step

Here is how to change the image's color tones—first globally and then in specific parts of the image.

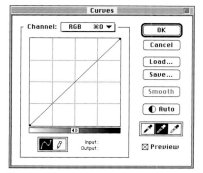

Select the gray eyedropper and click on the spot in the image you want to be neutral.

Double-click on the white eyedropper and enter the white point setting. As long as the R, G and B values are equal, the point is neutral, without color tinge.

Neutral gray

After the black and white points have been adjusted (see the section on tone correction on page 65), it is time to adjust the color balance of the image to eliminate undesirable color tinges. Use the gray eyedropper and click on the spot in the image you want to be neutral. That part of the image will retain its brightness level, but the color balance of the image will change to make the spot neutral.

Another method is to choose *Levels* or *Curves* under *Adjust* (*Image* menu). Double-click on the white eyedropper in the dialog box and feed in an RGB value high enough that you get the desired CMYK values for a neutral highlight tone. The fact that the R values, G values and B values are alike means that the tone is neutral. The separation settings you use determine which CMYK values these RGB values correspond to. Then click on the spot in the image that you want to be the neutral highlight point. The image adjusts and any color tinges disappear. The pixels in the image that are pure white, that is, lighter than the tone you clicked on, will remain white.

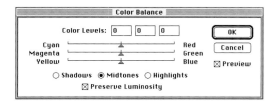

Color balance

If the determination of highlight points is not enough to remove color tinges, you can use the *Color Balance* dialog under *Adjust*. First, the midtones must be adjusted. When you chose *Color Balance*, the small radio button entitled *Midtones* was selected as the default. Adjust the color balance by moving the slider controls.

The image before applying selective color correction for the red tones.

The image after correcting the red tones.

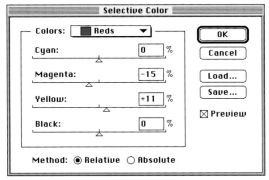

Skin tones in the image are dominated by red.

Selective color correction

The next step is to remove the color cast found in certain colors. These might occur if, for example, the skin tones in an image were too red, but the image in general was not too red. To remove the cast, use the *Selective Color* dialog box. Find out which basic color dominates the color you wish to alter. Use the [*Show*] *Info* palette and set it to show both RBG and CMYK values.

Open the dialog box for *Selective Color* under *Adjust* (*Image* menu). Choose the dominant color from the *Colors* menu. Adjust the composition of the color using the four slider controls for the process colors. If the *Relative* radio button is selected, the changes will take place relative to the values the pixels had before the change. If the *Absolute* button is selected, the same amount of color is added or subtracted regardless of the values the pixels had before. With *Relative*, in other words, the differences between the pixels are retained to a greater degree than they are with *Absolute*.

Sharpening, Step by Step

In Photoshop, the best tool for increasing image sharpness is the Unsharp Mask *filter. It affects either parts of the selected image or the entire image. To avoid sharpening small dirt particles in the image, you can enter a threshold value. Also, the* Amount *and* Radius *values of the filter can be changed.*

Too little sharpness

Correct sharpness

Too much sharpness

Unsharp mask

Choose *Unsharp Mask* from the *Sharpen* menu (*Filter* menu).

Preview

Use the preview displayed in the dialog box to determine the correct threshold, amount and radius values. A rather good threshold value to start with is 7. A suitable radius is just under 1.0; try 0.7. The amount of sharpening can vary. The higher the figure, the more sharpening. Start with a value around 170%. The best viewing scale to determine if the sharpness is sufficient is 1:1. The viewing scale is found under the *Preview* window. At a scale of 1:1, each pixel in the image is displayed as a pixel on the screen. If you check the *Preview* box, the degree of sharpness will be applied to the entire image in the background.

Correct scale

The image will be quite large with a scale set at 1:1, so it may be better to view the entire image after using the sharpening filter with the viewing scale set at 1:2 to get a better idea of the sharpness. If a smaller scale is used, the low resolution of the monitor screen will cause undesirable sharpness effects to be greatly reinforced. This will not be evident when printed, since the printing resolution is so much higher. A sign of excessive sharpness can be detected around edges, which become too pronounced and take on a shadow effect.

Undo and redo

If the sharpness fails to come out right, undo the filter and try again with different values. Avoid sharpening several times in a row without undoing. It is better to undo and start over with new values.

A good image with good resolution and sharpness can take quite a bit of electronic sharpening. But images with poor tonal differences and poor detail easily become worse if sharpening is attempted too often.

Separation, Step by Step

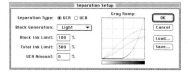

This is how the *Separation Setup* dialog box (*Preferences*) looks in Photoshop. It is used to determine the separation method to be used, either GCR or UCR. The *Black Generation* menu controls how much black will be generated in separation, that is, the achromatic degree.

The *Black Ink Limit* value controls the maximum tonal value for black depicted in the film. The *Total Ink Limit* value controls the total maximum permitted density of ink depicted. The UCA radio button determines the amount of primary color to be added.

The diagram shows the composition of the neutral gray shades. The horizontal axis represents the desired gray shades, and the vertical axis their composition.

By choosing *Custom* from the *Black Generation* menu, it is possible to control black generation by drawing your own curve.

The *Load* and *Save* buttons are used to load and save black generation curves and settings.

Printing Inks

Make sure that the correct inks for your printing conditions have been selected.

In the U.S., SWOP standard coated is best for coated paper, and SNAP works best for newsprint. In Europe, the Eurostandard (Coated) is best for coated paper, and Eurostandard (Newsprint) works best for newspapers. Each set of inks has its own preset dot gain, and the gray balance is unchanged (all values are 1.0). Enter the dot gain that applies to the press you are using. If you wish to change the gray balance, enter a value other than 1.0 in the box of the ink whose amount you wish to increase or decrease. For example, entering 0.9 in the box for magenta will result in less magenta in the finished photo.

Separation method

Choose *Separation Setup* and select the desired level for GCR or UCR and enter the maximum *Total Ink Limit*. For GCR, the *Light* or *Medium* levels (in the *Black Generation* menu) are often suitable. For newsprint, the *Heavy* setting may work well. *Maximum* is used only when separating color line art. That setting results in thin black lines being built up of black ink alone, thus avoiding lack of sharpness and off-register errors. The *Total Ink Limit* should not be reduced to a level so low that the color curves flatten out into the dark tones. Then not enough ink will end up on the paper to reproduce the tones correctly. If you wish to reduce the *Total Ink Limit*, choose a higher GCR level.

Separation Tables

Normally the printing ink parameters and the separation settings are adjusted only once for each printing process. If several different printing processes are used, it may be advisable to save the parameters in a separation table. This can be done, once the correct parameters have been set, by selecting *Separation Tables* under *Preferences* in the *File* menu and clicking on *Save*. All the settings for printing inks and separation will then be saved in a separation table. After saving the table, you can click on *Acquire* under the *File* menu to load it. The values in the table will then supersede the values shown in the *Printing Inks Setup*. The values for *Separation Setup* cannot be altered. The dot gain for grayscale images will, however, be affected, if, that is, the box for *Use Dot Gain for Grayscale Images* has been checked.

Tables from suppliers other than Adobe can also be accessed by using the *Acquire* option (under *File*). If such tables have been loaded, methods for converting from RGB and CMYK other than those that Photoshop normally employs are used. This often gives better results.

RGB to CMYK

When you have ensured that the correct parameters have been set, you can convert from RGB to CMYK by choosing *CMYK Color* under the *Mode* menu.

Background Stripping with Pen

Removing the background around an object to make it fit a layout is very common. It is usually called "background stripping." There are several ways of doing this in Photoshop. Two of them are described here. The pen tool is used for rough stripping, and masks are used for jobs requiring precision.

Show paths

Choose [*Show*] *Paths* from the *Window* menu and click on the pen tool.

Draw a connected path

Create a connected path by clicking with the pen tool along the contour of the object. If you miss and wish to remove the last point, press the backspace key. When you want to draw the new point, you first must click exactly on the previous point to make the path continuous.

Draw several paths if the background stripping is complex, or if it contains several objects. You can also use the pen tool to make a curving path segment.

Save the path

Choose *Save Path* from the *Paths* menu and give the path a suitable name. All the paths that are shown then will be saved under that name.

Clipping path

Choose *Clipping Path* from the *Paths* menu and select the path you just saved. Enter a suitable value for *Flatness*. The lower the value, the higher the precision but also the more difficult it is for the RIP to calculate. A value of 3 should be about right. If a PostScript error occurs during image output, it is often caused by a *Flatness* value that is too low for the amount of memory in the RIP. The clipping path turns everything outside its borders transparent.

White background

If you wish to remove the stripped background—making it white on the monitor screen—choose *Make Selection* from the *Paths* menu.

Then choose *Inverse* from the Photoshop *Select* menu to select everything you want to remove instead of what you wish to keep. Press the backspace key.

Actually, you do not need to make the background white manually since the clipping path will automatically see to it that the background disappears (becomes transparent) when the image is mounted in a program such as QuarkXPress. Nonetheless, it may be beneficial to see how it looks in Photoshop. Moreover, if large background areas have been removed from the image, it may be good to crop it to prevent taking up excessive storage space.

Background Stripping with Mask

If greater stripping precision is required to make the transition from object to background smoother, or if the object to be stripped has many small protrusions, it is best to use the mask function to create the selection prior to stripping.

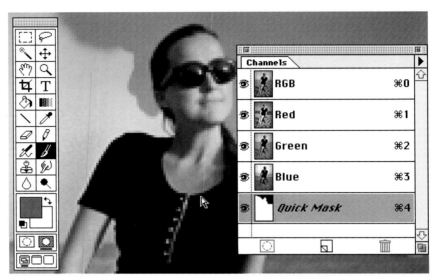

Paint a mask

Paint a mask over the background to be stripped away. The simplest way to do this is to click on the brush tool (tool palette), the size and properties of which can be varied with the [*Show*] *Brushes* palette (if you want soft stripping, use a soft brush—a pressure sensitive pen is better for this work than a mouse). Then click on the mask symbol in the tool palette before painting.

Invert mask

You can invert the mask by holding down the Option key and clicking on the mask symbol again. This will make it easier to see the border between the object and the background.

Working with only the mask

Open [*Show*] *Channels* in the *Palettes* menu and remove the eyes for all the channels except the mask by clicking on them. You will then see the mask in black. This may be advantageous if you wish to improve the mask without being distracted by the image. Click the eyes back for the RGB or CMYK channels when you want to see the whole image again. Make sure the pen tool is not visible for these channels; if it is, then the changes you make in the mask will affect the image itself.

Make a selection

When you have finished the stripping mask, select it by clicking on the selection symbol in the tool palette.

Transparent background

If you want a transparent background, you must choose *Make Path* under the *Paths* menu. Handle the path as you would when using the pen tool (page 71).

Remove background

If you wish to remove the background, make sure it is selected and then press the backspace key. If you mistakenly select the object, choose *Inverse* under the *Select* menu and then press the backspace key.

Wirephoto, Step by Step

A Macintosh PowerBook and a small CCD image scanner can be advantageously used by press photographers out on assignment to send photos back to their editors. Here is a brief description of how to do this. The following software is used: Adobe Photoshop 3.0, SprintScan plug-in for Polaroid SprintScan 35, and Microphone LT.

Maximum size (in inches) if the entire negative is printed in the newspaper with the stated resolution (dots per inch) and screen frequency (lines per inch).

Screen	Resolution				
	675	1012	1350	2025	2700
75	6.5x4.3	9.7x6.5	12.9x8.6	19.4x12.9	25.9x17.2
85	5.7x3.8	10.7x7.1	11.4x7.6	17.1x11.4	22.8x15.2
100	4.8x3.2	7.3x4.9	9.7x6.5	14.6x9.7	19.4x12.9

Scanning the image

Choose *Acquire— SprintScan 35* under the Photoshop *File* menu. Select the type of film that was used and click on *Preview*. Crop the image by drawing a cropping rectangle with the cropping tool. Click on automatic exposure (diaphragm symbol) and choose a suitable resolution (see table). Then click *Scan*. The image will be scanned and displayed on the display screen.

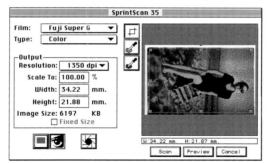

File information

Choose *File Info* under the *File* menu and enter the photo caption. There are five different info categories in a pop-up menu that follow IPTC standards, the most common type used by newspapers. Choose the category you want. Click on *OK* when finished.

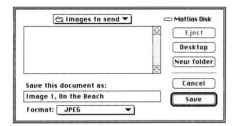 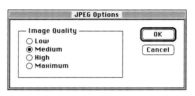

Compression

Choose *Save As* under the *File* menu. A pop-up menu in the displayed dialog box shows the available file formats. Select *JPEG*. Give the file a suitable name and click on *Save*. A new box will be displayed in which you can choose how much the image is to be compressed. Select *Medium* if you want a small file and *High* if you give priority to quality over a short transmission time.

Connection

Connect the computer's modem and a telephone to a convenient phone jack. You will then be able to use one phone line for both voice and data communication. You'll be able to speak over the phone before transmitting images.

Start the communications program

Start Microphone and check that all the settings are correct for your computer.

Calling up

Call your home office and ask someone to call you back. When the phone rings, answer it. If the phone signal has created strange characters in the Microphone window, you can reset Microphone by typing ATZ on a new line and pressing the return key.

Getting ready to send

When you are ready to start sending, type ATD and press Return. When you hear that your modem is transmitting, hang up the phone. (If *Local Echo* has been turned on, you will see double letters on the screen.) At the same time, the person at the other end should know to type ATA, press return, and hang up the phone. The two modems will then communicate and, with any luck, you will see *Connect* appear on the screen. If the process is not working, check that your *Communications* settings under the *Settings* menu are correct for your computer. Under difficult transmission conditions, it may be necessary to try several times. Reducing the baud rate may help.

Sending an image

With communications established, choose *Send* from the *Transfer* menu and find and select the image file to be sent. Make sure ZMODEM has been chosen as the protocol. Then click *Send*. Image transmission will start, and a box showing the remaining time will be displayed.

When the image has been sent, you can send another in the same way or you can disconnect by choosing *Hang Up* from the *Phone* menu.

Photoshop Memory Tips

Photoshop 3.0 handles memory first by using the computer's RAM and then by using the hard disk or disks assigned with the Scratch Disks *command under* Preferences *(File menu).*

Select the Photoshop icon in the Adobe Photoshop folder and choose *Get Info* under the Finder's *File* menu. Here you can change the *Memory Requirements* to suit your computer.

Example

Assume you are going to work on an image that takes up 10 MB of memory.

Memory allocation

When Photoshop starts up, it will use 5 MB of operating memory for itself (stated as *Minimum* in the *Get Info* box). Another 10 MB will be used for the image. In other words, you must give Photoshop at least 12 MB (as per the *Preferred* value in the *Get Info* box) in order to be able to open a 10-MB image all in RAM.

Temporary files

In addition, temporary (scratch) files are opened on the hard disk assigned under the *Scratch Disks* command (see above). When you carry out certain commands in Photoshop, the program creates several temporary files—as many as four. Each file is as big as the image. At maximum, Photoshop will require five times as much memory as the image takes up. It does not make any difference whether this is RAM or hard disk memory. Of course, RAM is always much faster. Thus, the more RAM Photoshop uses, the faster your work will go. When you create a new layer, the same amount of memory is used for each new layer as is used by the image without extra layers.

Several images at once

If you open several images at the same time, it is their total collective memory requirement that is to be multiplied by five to arrive at the maximum memory allocation. With limited amounts of memory, in other words, it is faster to work with one image at a time.

What kind of memory should you have?

RAM is the most expensive kind of memory, which is why it may suffice to buy enough RAM to work with normal-size images and then be sure that you have a very fast hard disk to cope with big images. This is less expensive than trying to cope with all image sizes using RAM. A hard disk that is used as a scratch disk ought not be too fragmented (writing and reading of the disk will slow down). It is recommended that you regularly use a program such as Speed Disk to achieve optimal hard-disk speeds.

Photos by Ingemar Lindewall

Photos by Lars Germundson

Photos by Lotte Fernvall

Many thanks to: **Lars Germundson**/Grafisk Assistans for fact checking and the theories on original types; **Micke Falck** for fact checking; **Hans Olsson**, **Chadwa Kazunga** and **Peter Wärn**/Software Plus for valuable comments; **Mark Crowley**/ Q.S.S., Limited for answering questions about QuarkXPress; **Lotte Fernvall**, **Lasse Hedberg**, **Bo Hedin** and **Mats Strand** at Aftonbladet; **Klasse Lindberg** and **Fredrik Linder** at IGP; **Jon Dranger** for illustrations, and **Anders Blomberg** for illustrations, drawings and graphics; and **Linda Hoflin**.

The photos in this book have been color corrected, processed and color separated using Adobe Photoshop and Cachet. The illustrations were done using Adobe Illustrator. QuarkXPress was used for page layout. The finished films were produced with an Agfa SelectSet Avantra 25 at IGP in Stockholm. Copy was typeset using *Adobe Minion* 10/12.5. *Franklin Gothic* 8/9.5 from Adobe was used for the photo captions. The pages were printed on Gallery Art 135g and the cover on Invercote GX 230g at Rolf & Co. in Skövde, Sweden.

Index

Italics are used for the names of commands, dialog boxes, etc. **Bold** is used for the page numbers containing the most important information pertaining to the key word listed.

More from Peachpit Press

ColorCourse Interactive Training CDs
ColorExpert
ColorCourse/Photography demonstrates how to evaluate, scan, and separate photos for faithful reproduction. *ColorCourse/Illustration* covers trapping, scaling, blends, scanning specifications, and proofing. *ColorCourse/Imagesetting* focuses on getting the best final output possible with tips on topics like film imaging, proofing, quality assurance, and working with service bureaus. Includes a comprehensive trouble-shooting guide. Fully indexed with text links throughout. *$49.95 each (CD-ROM)*

A Day with Biff
Ron Romain and Joe Crabtree
It's a dog-eat-dog world. Just ask Biff, a protagonist pooch that's leapt paws first into the puzzling, amusing world of humans at work. Superb usable, original, clip-art makes this whimsical interactive book/disk package a joy. Like any good bad dog, Biff takes his job—distracting you from the task at hand—very seriously. His weapons: a maze, a treasure hunt, and more. Now play! *$24.95 (96 pages, w/disk)*

The Illustrator 5.0/5.5 Book
Deke McClelland
Experienced Illustrator users and novices alike will learn many helpful tips and techniques. Very thorough and comprehensive, *The Illustrator 5.0/5.5 Book* gives in-depth coverage of Illustrator's latest features. *$29.95 (660 pages)*

Illustrator Illuminated, 2nd Edition
Clay Andres
Illustrator Illuminated uses full-color graphics to show how professional artists use Illustrator's tools to create a variety of styles and effects. Each chapter shows the creation of a specific illustration from concept through completion. Additionally, it covers using Illustrator in conjunction with Adobe Streamline and Photoshop. *$27.95 (200 pages)*

The Macintosh Bible, 5th Edition
Edited by Darcy DiNucci
This classic reference book is now completely updated. *The Macintosh Bible, 5th Edition* is crammed with tips, tricks, and shortcuts that will help you to get the most out of your Mac. $30 *(1,100 pages)*

The Official Photo CD Handbook:
A Verbum Interactive Guide
Michael Gosney, et all.
With Photo CD, Kodak's breakthrough technology, you don't have to wait for tomorrow's electronic cameras to join the digital photography revolution. Learn how to use and store digital images and media files without spending a fortune. Two CDs include mutimedia presentations, valuable Photo CD utilities, and 68 MB of usable images, backgrounds and sounds. *$39.95 (384 pages, w/2 CD-ROMs)*

Photoshop 3 for Macintosh:
Visual QuickStart Guide
Elaine Weinmann and Peter Lourekas
Completely revised for Photoshop 3, this indispensable guide is for Mac users who want to get started in Adobe Photoshop but don't like to read long explanations. QuickStart books focus on illustrated, step-by-step examples that cover how to use masks, filters, colors, and more. *$19.95 (264 pages)*

The Photoshop 3 Wow! Book (Mac Edition)
Linnea Dayton and Jack Davis
This book is really two books in one: an easy-to-follow, step-by-step tutorial of Photoshop fundamentals and over 150 pages of tips and techniques for getting the most out of Photoshop version 3. Full color throughout, *The Photoshop 3 Wow! Book* shows how professional artists make the best use of Photoshop. Includes a CD-ROM containing Photoshop filters and utilities. *$39.95 (208 pages, w/CD-ROM)*

Photoshop in Black and White, 2nd Edition
Jim Rich and Sandy Bozek
Updated to cover versions 2.5 and 3.0, this book explains how to adjust black-and-white images of any type for reproduction. Topics inlude image characteristics; adjusting highlights, shadows, and midtones; sharpening images; and converting from color to greyscale. Appendices cover scanning, resampling and calibration. *$18 (44 pages)*

The QuarkXPress Book, 4th Edition
(Mac Edition)
David Blatner and Eric Taub
This is the highest rated, most comprehensive, and best-selling QuarkXPress book ever published. Now totally updated to cover the newest version, this book is made for easy access, including a handy tear-out keystroke shortcut card. You'll find valuable information on XTensions, EfiColor, AppleEvent scripting and more. Winner of the 1991 Benjamin Franklin Award (computer book category). *$29.95 (784 pages)*

QuarkXPress Tips & Tricks, 2nd Edition
David Blatner and Eric Taub
The smartest, most useful shortcuts from *The QuarkXPress Book*—plus many more—are packed into this book. You'll find answers to common questions as well as insights on techniques that will show you how to become a QuarkXPress power user. Includes a CD-ROM with useful XTensions and demos. *$34.95 (286 pages, w/CD-ROM)*

Real World Scanning and Halftones
David Blatner and Steve Roth
Master the digital halftone process—from scanning images to tweaking them on your computer to imagesetting them. Learn about optical character recognition, gamma control, sharpening, PostScript halftones, Photo CD and image-manipulating applications like Photoshop and PhotoStyler. *$24.95 (296 pages)*

Order Form

USA 800-283-9444 • 510-548-4393 • FAX 510-548-5991
CANADA 800-387-8028 • 416-447-1779 • FAX 800-456-0536 OR 416-443-0948

Qty	Title	Price	Total
	SUBTOTAL		
	ADD APPLICABLE SALES TAX*		
	SHIPPING		
	TOTAL		

Shipping is by UPS ground: $4 for first item, $1 each add'l.

*We are required to pay sales tax in all states with the exceptions of AK, DE, HI, MT, NH, NV, OK, OR, SC and WY. Please include appropriate sales tax if you live in any state not mentioned above.

Customer Information

NAME

COMPANY

STREET ADDRESS

CITY   STATE   ZIP

PHONE ( )   FAX ( )
[REQUIRED FOR CREDIT CARD ORDERS]

Payment Method

❑ CHECK ENCLOSED   ❑ VISA   ❑ MASTERCARD   ❑ AMEX

CREDIT CARD #   EXP. DATE

COMPANY PURCHASE ORDER #

Tell Us What You Think

PLEASE TELL US WHAT YOU THOUGHT OF THIS BOOK: TITLE:_____

WHAT OTHER BOOKS WOULD YOU LIKE US TO PUBLISH?

MAC   PEACHPIT PRESS • 2414 Sixth Street • Berkeley, CA 94710